EVERY DAY MATH PRACTICE FOR GRADES 1-3

1000+ QUESTIONS YOU NEED TO KILL IN ⇒ ELEMENTARY SCHOOL

made by
Brain Hunter Prep
with love from New York

Books made by Brain Hunter Prep with love from New York

GRADE 1-3

GRADE 4-5
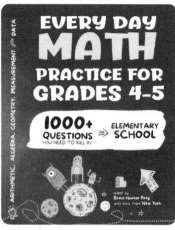

GRADE 6-8

We take great pride in providing our students, parents and educators with the best educational products and customer service. We kindly ask for one minute of your time to leave us an honest review on Amazon for this workbook.

Reviews help us grow our brand, improve our products, and allow customers to learn more about our workbooks. Thanks for letting us be a part of your child's educational journey.

TABLE OF CONTENTS

Operations and Algebraic Thinking 8

Addition and Subtraction 10

Multiplication and Division 28

Applying Operations to Solve Word Problems 50

Numbers and Operations in Base Ten **62**

Counting 64

Number Forms 70

Rounding 72

Number Sense and Place Value 74

Compare by looking at 100, 10, 1s (<, >, =) 88

Using place value to perform operations 90

Numbers, Operations, and Fractions **110**

Dividing Shapes into Equal Parts 112

Understanding Fractions 134

Comparing Fractions 155

Measurement and Data **166**

Measurement of Objects 168

Area and Perimeter 191

Measurement of Time 202

Measurement of Data 210

Measurement Word Problems 215

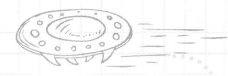

Check out our ArgoPrep brand workbooks!

All of our workbooks come equipped with detailed video explanations to make your learning experience a breeze! Visit us at www.argoprep.com

COMMON CORE SERIES

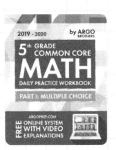   

SPECIALIZED HIGH SCHOOL ADMISSIONS TEST

HIGHER LEVEL EXAMS

INTRODUCING MATH!

Introducing Math! by ArgoPrep is an award-winning series created by certified teachers to provide students with high-quality practice problems. These workbooks include topic overviews with instruction, practice questions, answer explanations along with digital access to video explanations. Practice in confidence - with ArgoPrep!

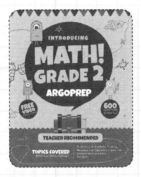

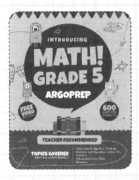

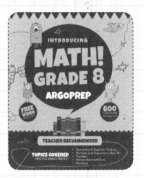

YOGA MINDFULNESS

If you are looking for a fun way to engage with your children while helping them build a mindful, engaged and healthy lifestyle, Frogyogi's Yoga Stories for Kids and Parents is the perfect book for you and your family!

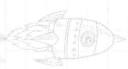

KIDS SUMMER ACADEMY SERIES

ArgoPrep's **Kids Summer Academy** series helps prevent summer learning loss and gets students ready for their new school year by reinforcing core foundations in math, english and science. Our workbooks also introduce new concepts so students can get a head start and be on top of their game for the new school year!

Meet the ArgoPrep heroes.

Are you ready to go on an incredible adventure and complete your journey with them to become a **SUPER** student?

MYSTICAL NINJA

GREEN POISON

FIRESTORM WARRIOR

RAPID NINJA

CAPTAIN ARGO

THUNDER WARRIOR

ADRASTOS THE SUPER WARRIOR

Our **Kids Summer Academy** series by **ArgoPrep** is designed to keep students engaged with fun graphics and activities. Our curriculum is aligned with state standards to help your child prepare for their new school year.

Operations and Algebraic Thinking

1. **Addition and Subtraction** page 10

2. **Multiplication and Division** page 28

3. **Applying Operations to Solve Word Problems** page 50

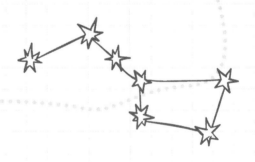

1. Which number is 3 more than 5?

   A. 10   **C.** 2
   B. 6   **D.** 8

Difficulty: Easy

2. Which number is 2 less than 8?

   A. 16   **C.** 6
   B. 4   **D.** 10

Difficulty: Easy

3. Which number is 4 more than 6?

   A. 2   **C.** 4
   B. 10   **D.** 12

Difficulty: Easy

4. Which number is 1 less than 9?

   A. 8   **C.** 2
   B. 10   **D.** 18

Difficulty: Easy

5. Which number is 3 more than 2?

   A. 5   **C.** 6
   B. 1   **D.** 4

Difficulty: Easy

6. What number is 5 more than 3?

   A. 7   **C.** 9
   B. 8   **D.** 10

Difficulty: Easy

7. What number is 7 less than 10?

   A. 1   **C.** 3
   B. 2   **D.** 4

Difficulty: Easy

8. What number is 2 more than 4?

   A. 9   **C.** 7
   B. 8   **D.** 6

Difficulty: Easy

9. What number is 6 less than 8?

   A. 4   **C.** 2
   B. 3   **D.** 1

Difficulty: Easy

10. Which number is even?

   A. 7   **C.** 6
   B. 3   **D.** 9

Difficulty: Medium

11. Which number is odd?

A. 2   C. 6
B. 3   D. 8

Difficulty: Medium

12. Which number is even?

A. 17   C. 11
B. 19   D. 12

Difficulty: Medium

13. Which number is even?

A. 14   C. 17
B. 15   D. 9

Difficulty: Medium

14. Which number is odd?

A. 12   C. 15
B. 14   D. 16

Difficulty: Medium

15. Which number is odd?

A. 5   C. 2
B. 6   D. 8

Difficulty: Medium

16. Which number is even?

A. 13   C. 28
B. 25   D. 19

Difficulty: Medium

17. Which number is odd?

A. 20   C. 24
B. 23   D. 30

Difficulty: Medium

1. Explanation: To solve this problem, you should count up three numbers starting at 5: 5, 6, 7, 8. Three numbers past 5 is 8.

   The correct answer is D.

2. Explanation: To solve this problem, you should count down two numbers starting at 8: 8, 7, 6. Two numbers below 8 is 6.

   The correct answer is C.

3. Explanation: To solve this problem, you should count up four numbers starting at 6: 6, 7, 8, 9, 10. Four numbers above 6 is 10.

   The correct answer is B.

4. Explanation: To solve this problem, you should count down one number starting at 9: 9, 8. One number below 9 is 8.

   The correct answer is A.

5. Explanation: To solve this problem, you should count up 3 numbers starting at 2: 2, 3, 4, 5. Three numbers above 2 is 5.

   The correct answer is A.

6. Explanation: To solve this problem, you should count up 5 numbers starting at 3: 3, 4, 5, 6, 7, 8. Five numbers above 3 is 8.

   The correct answer is B.

7. Explanation: To solve this problem, you should count down 7 numbers starting at 10: 10, 9, 8, 7, 6, 5, 4, 3. Seven numbers below 10 is 3.

   The correct answer is C.

8. Explanation: To solve this problem, you should count up 2 numbers starting at 4: 4, 5, 6. Two numbers above four is 6.

   The correct answer is D.

9. Explanation: To solve this problem, you should count down 6 numbers starting at 8: 8, 7, 6, 5, 4, 3, 2. Six numbers below 8 is 2.

   The correct answer is C.

10. Explanation: Even numbers are divisible by 2 and end in 2, 4, 6, 8, 0. Odd numbers are not divisible by 2 and end in 1, 3, 5, 7, 9. 6 is even because it is divisible by 2.

The correct answer is C.

11. Explanation: Even numbers are divisible by 2 and end in 2, 4, 6, 8, 0. Odd numbers are not divisible by 2 and end in 1, 3, 5, 7, 9. 3 is odd because it is not divisible by 2.

The correct answer is B.

12. Explanation: Even numbers are divisible by 2 and end in 2, 4, 6, 8, 0. Odd numbers are not divisible by 2 and end in 1, 3, 5, 7, 9. 12 is even because it ends in 2.

The correct answer is D.

13. Explanation: Even numbers are divisible by 2 and end in 2, 4, 6, 8, 0. Odd numbers are not divisible by 2 and end in 1, 3, 5, 7, 9. 14 is even because it ends in 4.

The correct answer is A.

14. Explanation: Even numbers are divisible by 2 and end in 2, 4, 6, 8, 0. Odd numbers are not divisible by 2 and end in 1, 3, 5, 7, 9. 15 is odd because it ends in 5.

The correct answer is C.

15. Explanation: Even numbers are divisible by 2 and end in 2, 4, 6, 8, 0. Odd numbers are not divisible by 2 and end in 1, 3, 5, 7, 9. 5 is odd because it is not divisible by 2.

The correct answer is A.

16. Explanation: Even numbers are divisible by 2 and end in 2, 4, 6, 8, 0. Odd numbers are not divisible by 2 and end in 1, 3, 5, 7, 9. 28 is even because it ends in 8.

The correct answer is C.

17. Explanation: Even numbers are divisible by 2 and end in 2, 4, 6, 8, 0. Odd numbers are not divisible by 2 and end in 1, 3, 5, 7, 9. 23 is odd because it ends in 3.

The correct answer is B.

1. Which number is odd?

A. 20   C. 10

B. 100   D. ①

Difficulty: Medium

2. 7 + 6 = 13

A. 10   C. 12

B. 11   D. ⑬

Difficulty: Easy

3. 11 - 3 = 8

A. 7   C. 9

B. ⑧   D. 10

Difficulty: Easy

4. 1 + 4 = 5

A. ⑤   C. 7

B. 6   D. 8

Difficulty: Easy

5. 9 - 7 = 2

A. ②   C. 4

B. 3   D. 5

Difficulty: Easy

6. 19 - 9 = 10

A. 13   C. 11

B. 12   D. ⑩

Difficulty: Easy

7. 2 + 3 = 5

A. 6   C. 4
B. (5)   D. 3

Difficulty: Easy

8. 8 - 4 = 4

A. 6   C. (4)
B. 5   D. 3

Difficulty: Easy

9. 10 - 6 = 4

A. (4)   C. 6
B. 5   D. 7

Difficulty: Easy

10. 5 + 1 = 6

A. 9   C. 7
B. 8   D. (6)

Difficulty: Easy

11. 7 + 7 = 14

A. 13   C. 15
B. (14)   D. 16

Difficulty: Medium

12. 15 - 3 = 12

A. 14   C. (12)
B. 13   D. 11

Difficulty: Medium

13. 9 + 8 = 17

A. (17)   C. 19
B. 18   D. 20

Difficulty: Medium

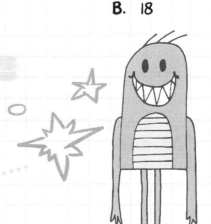

1. Explanation: Even numbers are divisible by **2** and end in **2, 4, 6, 8, 0**. Odd numbers are not divisible by **2** and end in **1, 3, 5, 7, 9**.

   The correct answer is D.

2. Explanation: To solve this problem, you should count the number of trees there are total, which will give you **13**.

   The correct answer is D.

3. Explanation: To solve this problem, you should count the books that are left when you cross out three, which will give you **8**.

   The correct answer is B.

4. Explanation: To solve this problem, you should count the total number of children, which will give you **5**.

   The correct answer is A.

5. Explanation: To solve this problem, you should count the number of cars that are left when you cross off **7**, which will give you **2**.

   The correct answer is A.

6. Explanation: To solve this problem, you should count the number of houses that are left when you cross off **9**, which will give you **10**.

   The correct answer is D.

7. Explanation: To solve this problem, you should count the number of total animals, cats and dogs, which will give you **5**.

   The correct answer is B.

8. Explanation: To solve this problem, you should count the number of globes there are when you cross off 4, which will give you 4.

   The correct answer is C.

9. Explanation: To solve this problem, you should count the number of cameras that are left when you cross off six, which will give you 4.

   The correct answer is A.

10. Explanation: To solve this problem, you should count the number of hats there are total, which will give you 6.

    The correct answer is D.

11. Explanation: To solve this problem, you can count up seven from seven, which gives you 14.

    The correct answer is B.

12. Explanation: To solve this problem, you can count down three from fifteen, which gives you 12.

    The correct answer is C.

13. Explanation: To solve this problem, you should count up eight from nine, which will give you 17.

    The correct answer is A.

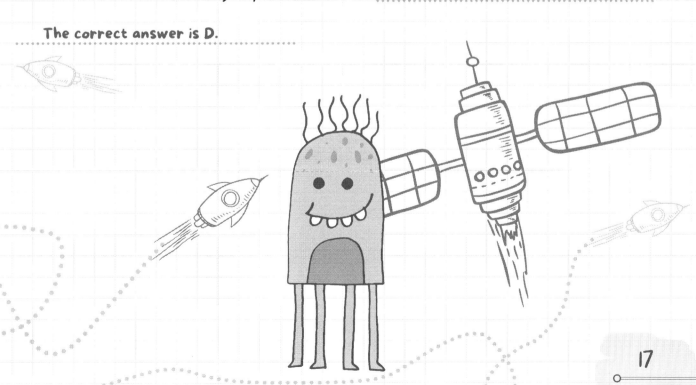

1. 7 - 5 = 2

   A. 4   C. (2)
   B. 3   D. 1

   Difficulty: Medium

2. 14 + 3 =

   A. 16   C. 18
   B. (17)   D. 19

   Difficulty: Medium

3. 11 + 2 = 13

   A. 9   C. 12
   B. 10   D. (13)

   Difficulty: Easy

4. 10 - 3 =

   A. 10   C. 8
   B. 9   D. 7

   Difficulty: Easy

5. 17 - 8 =

   A. 9   C. 11
   B. 10   D. 12

   Difficulty: Easy

6. 6 + 4 = 10

   A. 14   C. (10)
   B. 12   D. 11

   Difficulty: Easy

7. 5 + 2 + 1 =

   A. 5   C. 7
   B. 6   D. (8)

   Difficulty: Easy

8. 3 + 7 + 6

   A. 16   C. 18
   B. 17   D. 19

   Difficulty: Easy

9. 4 + 2 + 8 =

   A. 16   C. 14
   B. 15   D. 13

   Difficulty: Easy

10. 6 + 9 + 3 =

    A. 15   C. 17
    B. 16   D. 18

    Difficulty: Easy

11. 8 + 6 + 2 =

- A. 15
- B. 16
- C. 17
- D. 18

Difficulty: Easy

12. 1 + 5 + 8 =

- A. 14
- B. 15
- C. 16
- D. 13

Difficulty: Easy

13. 4 + 7 + 2 =

- A. 13
- B. 12
- C. 11
- D. 10

Difficulty: Easy

14. 9 + 3 + 6 =

- A. 17
- B. 18
- C. 16
- D. 15

Difficulty: Easy

15. 2 + 6 + 5 =

- A. 10
- B. 11
- C. 12
- D. 13

Difficulty: Easy

16. Which problem can be used to help solve 4 + 5 + 6?

- A. 4 + 6
- B. 4 - 6
- C. 6 - 4
- D. 4 + 4

Difficulty: Easy

17. Which problem can be used to help solve 2 + 9 + 8?

- A. 10 + 2
- B. 8 + 8
- C. 2 + 8
- D. 2 + 2

Difficulty: Easy

18. Which problem provides the same answer as 3 + 7?

- A. 3 + 3
- B. 7 + 7
- C. 7 + 3
- D. 3 + 10

Difficulty: Easy

19. Which problem provides the same answer as 2 + 11?

- A. 2 + 2
- B. 11 + 2
- C. 11 + 1
- D. 13 + 2

Difficulty: Easy

1. Explanation: To solve this problem, you can count down five from seven, which gives you 2.

    The correct answer is C.

2. Explanation: To solve this problem, you can count up three from 14, which gives you 17.

    The correct answer is B.

3. Explanation: To solve this problem, you can count up two from 11, which gives you 13.

    The correct answer is D.

4. Explanation: To solve this problem, you can count down three from ten, which gives you seven.

    The correct answer is D.

5. Explanation: To solve this problem, you can count down eight from seventeen, which gives you 9.

    The correct answer is A.

6. Explanation: To solve this problem, you can count up four from six, which gives you 10.

    The correct answer is C.

7. Explanation: $5 + 2 = 7$, $7 + 1 = 8$

    The correct answer is D.

8. Explanation: $3 + 7 = 10$, $10 + 6 = 16$

    The correct answer is A.

9. Explanation: $4 + 2 = 6$, $6 + 8 = 14$

    The correct answer is C.

10. Explanation: $6 + 9 = 15$, $15 + 3 = 18$

    The correct answer is D.

11. Explanation: $8 + 6 = 14$, $14 + 2 = 16$

    The correct answer is B.

12. Explanation: 1 + 5 = 6, 6 + 8 = 14

    The correct answer is A.

13. Explanation: 4 + 7 = 11, 11 + 2 = 13

    The correct answer is A.

14. Explanation: 9 + 3 = 12, 12 + 6 = 18

    The correct answer is B.

15. Explanation: 2 + 6 = 8, 8 + 5 = 13

    The correct answer is D.

16. Explanation: Order does not matter when you add. 4 + 6 + 5 is the same problem as 4 + 5 + 6.

    The correct answer is A.

17. Explanation: Order does not matter when you add. 2 + 8 + 9 is the same problem as 2 + 9 + 8.

    The correct answer is C.

18. Explanation: Order does not matter when you add. 3 + 7 is the same problem as 7 + 3.

    The correct answer is C.

19. Explanation: Order does not matter when you add. 2 + 11 is the same problem as 11 + 2

    The correct answer is B.

1. Which problem can be used to help solve 5 + 2 + 5?

A. 5 + 5   C. 7 + 7

B. 2 + 2   D. 12 + 12

Difficulty: Easy

2. Which problem can be used to help solve 3 + 6 + 3?

A. 6 + 12   C. 3 + 9

B. 3 + 3   D. 6 + 2

Difficulty: Easy

3. Which problem can be used to help solve 1 + 4 + 9?

A. 1 + 9   C. 10 + 1

B. 1 + 1   D. 9 + 10

Difficulty: Easy

4. Which problem provides the same answer as 5 + 9?

A. 10 + 10   C. 5 + 5

B. 9 + 9   D. 9 + 5

Difficulty: Easy

5. Which problem provides the same answer as 4 + 8?

A. 20 + 4   C. 8 + 4

B. 8 + 8   D. 4 + 4

Difficulty: Easy

6. Which problem uses the equal sign correctly?

A. 10 = 11   C. 10 = 3

B. 10 = 9   D. 10 = 10

Difficulty: Easy

7. Which problem uses the equal sign correctly?

A. 6 = 5   C. 11 = 11

B. 8 = 11   D. 11 = 13

Difficulty: Easy

8. Which problem uses the equal sign correctly?

A. 5 = 2 - 3   C. 5 = 2

B. 5 = 2 + 3   D. 5 = 3 + 1

Difficulty: Easy

9. Which problem uses the equal sign correctly?

A. 3 + 9 = 12   C. 3 = 12
B. 9 = 12   D. 3 - 9 = 12

Difficulty: Easy

10. Which problem uses the equal sign correctly?

A. 7 + 7 = 10 - 4
B. 7 + 7 = 12
C. 7 + 7 = 10 + 4
D. 7 = 10 + 4

Difficulty: Easy

11. What problem uses the equal sign correctly?

A. 4 + 2 = 10 - 6
B. 5 + 5 = 12 + 1
C. 1 + 5 = 10 - 5
D. 10 - 4 = 2 + 4

Difficulty: Easy

12. What problem uses the equal sign correctly?

A. 10 - 9 = 3 - 2
B. 10 - 9 = 8
C. 3 - 2 = 5
D. 3 + 2 = 10 - 9

Difficulty: Easy

13. What problem uses the equal sign correctly?

A. 3 + 4 = 5 + 3
B. 3 + 4 = 5 + 2
C. 5 + 2 = 5 + 3
D. 7 = 5 + 3

Difficulty: Easy

14. What problem uses the equal sign correctly?

A. 11 - 5 = 3 + 6
B. 6 + 4 = 11 - 5
C. 11 - 5 = 5 + 5
D. 11 - 5 = 3 + 3

Difficulty: Easy

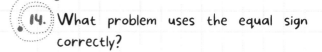
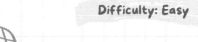

1. Explanation: Order does not matter when you add. 5 + 2 + 5 is the same problem as 5 + 5 + 2.

    The correct answer is A.

2. Explanation: Order does not matter when you add. 3 + 6 + 3 is the same problem as 3 + 3 + 6.

    The correct answer is B.

3. Explanation: Order does not matter when you add. 1 + 4 + 9 is the same problem as 1 + 9 + 4.

    The correct answer is A.

4. Explanation: Order does not matter when you add. 5 + 9 is the same problem as 9 + 5.

    The correct answer is D.

5. Explanation: Order does not matter when you add. 8 + 4 is the same problem as 4 + 8.

    The correct answer is C.

6. Explanation: The equal sign connects two facts that have the same value. In this case, 10 = 10 is the only set of numbers that have the same amount.

    The correct answer is D.

7. Explanation: The equal sign connects two facts that have the same value. In this case, 11 = 11 is the only set of numbers that have the same amount.

    The correct answer is C.

8. Explanation: The equal sign connects two facts that have the same value. In this case, 5 = 2 + 3 is the only set of numbers that have the same amount.

    The correct answer is B.

9. Explanation: The equal sign connects two facts that have the same value. In this case, 3 + 9 = 12 is the only set of numbers that have the same amount.

    The correct answer is A.

10. Explanation: The equal sign connects two facts that have the same value. In this case, 7 + 7 = 14 and 10 + 4 = 14 so this choice is the only set of facts that have the same amount.

The correct answer is C.

11. Explanation: The equal sign connects two facts that have the same value. In this case, 10 - 4 = 6 and 2 + 4 = 6 so this choice is the only set of facts that have the same amount.

The correct answer is D.

12. Explanation: The equal sign connects two facts that have the same value. In this case, 10 - 9 = 1 and 3 - 2 = 1 so this choice is the only set of facts that have the same amount.

The correct answer is A.

13. Explanation: The equal sign connects two facts that have the same value. In this case, 3 + 4 = 7 and 5 + 2 = 7 so this choice is the only set of facts that have the same amount.

The correct answer is B.

14. Explanation: The equal sign connects two facts that have the same value. In this case, 11 - 5 = 6 and 3 + 3 = 6 so this choice is the only set of facts that have the same amount.

The correct answer is D.

1. Which number makes this fact true?
? + 3 = 7

A. 4   C. 6
B. 5   D. 7

2. Which number makes this fact true?
? + 5 = 11

A. 3   C. 5
B. 4   D. 6

3. Which number makes this fact true?
10 - ? = 3

A. 8   C. 6
B. 7   D. 5

4. Which number makes this fact true?
14 + ? = 15

A. 1   C. 3
B. 2   D. 4

5. Which number makes this fact true?
17 - 7 = ?

A. 8   C. 10
B. 9   D. 11

6. Which number makes this fact true?
2 + ? = 8

A. 5   C. 7
B. 6   D. 8

7. Which number makes this fact true?
10 - 6 = ?

A. 4   C. 6
B. 5   D. 7

8. Which number makes this fact true?
? - 7 = 7

A. 14   C. 12
B. 13   D. 11

1. Explanation: The solution is 4 because
    4 + 3 = 7.

    The correct answer is A.

2. Explanation: The solution is 6 because
    6 + 5 = 11.

    The correct answer is D.

3. Explanation: The solution is 7 because
    10 - 7 = 3.

    The correct answer is B.

4. Explanation: The solution is 1 because
    14 + 1 = 15.

    The correct answer is A.

5. Explanation: The solution is 10 because
    17 - 7 = 10.

    The correct answer is C.

6. Explanation: The solution is 6 because
    2 + 6 = 8.

    The correct answer is B.

7. Explanation: The solution is 4 because
    10 - 6 = 4.

    The correct answer is A.

8. Explanation: The solution is 14 because
    14 - 7 = 7.

    The correct answer is A.

1. Which choice describes the number of circles?

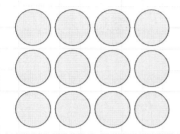

A. 3 + 4
B. 3 + 3 + 3
C. 2 + 2 + 2 + 2
D. 4 + 4 + 4 ✓

Difficulty: Medium

2. Which choice describes the number of triangles?

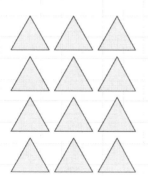

A. 3 + 3
B. 3 + 3 + 3 + 3 ✓
C. 3 + 3 + 3
D. 3 + 3 + 3 + 3 + 3

Difficulty: Medium

3. Which choice decides the number of squares?

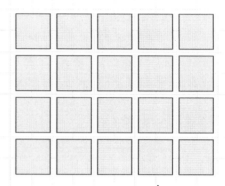

A. 5 + 5 + 5 + 5 20
B. 4 + 4 + 4
C. 5 + 4
D. 5 - 4

Difficulty: Medium

4. Which choice describes the number of stars?

A. 6 + 6 12
B. 2 + 6
C. 6 + 2
D. 6 + 6 + 6 + 6 + 6 + 6

Difficulty: Medium

5. Which choice describes the number of circles?

A. 3
B. 3 + 3
C. 3 + 3 + 3 q
D. 3 + 3 + 3 + 3

Difficulty: Medium

7. Which choice describes the number of hearts?

A. 2 + 2 + 2 + 2 8
B. 4 + 4 + 4 + 4
C. 2 + 2
D. 4 + 3 + 2

Difficulty: Medium

6. Which choice describes the number of stars?

A. 2 + 2 + 2   **C.** 2 + 2 + 5
B. 3 + 6   **D.** 5 + 5 10

Difficulty: Medium

8. Which choice describes the number of triangles?

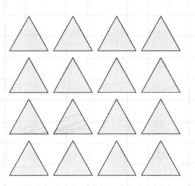

A. 4
B. 4 + 4 + 4 + 4 16
C. 4 + 4
D. 4 + 4 + 4

Difficulty: Medium

9. Which choice describes the number of rectangles?

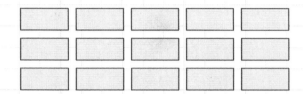

A. 5 + 3   **C.** 5 + 5

B. 3 + 3   **D.** 5 + 5 + 5

Difficulty: Medium

10. Which set of objects illustrates the problem 2 x 3?

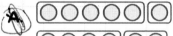

A.

B.

C.

D.

Difficulty: Hard

11. Which set of objects illustrates the problem 4 x 1?

A.

B.

C.

D.

Difficulty: Hard

12. Which set of objects illustrates the problem 5 x 6?

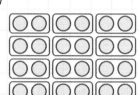

A.

B.

C.

D.

Difficulty: Hard

13. Which set of objects illustrates the problem 8 x 3?

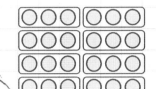

A.

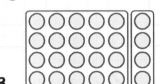

B.

C.

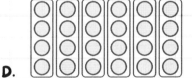

D.

Difficulty: Hard

14. Which set of objects illustrates the problem 2 x 9?

A.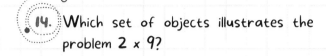

B.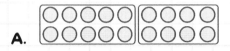

C.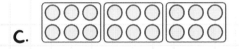

D.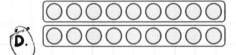

Difficulty: Hard

15. Which set of objects illustrates the problem 7 x 3?

A.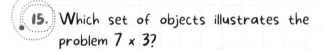

B.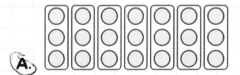

C.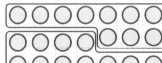

D.

Difficulty: Hard

1. Explanation: There are three lines of circles with 4 circles in each line. So to find the total number of circles, we should add 4 + 4 + 4, which equals 12. To check, count and you will see there are 12 circles.

The correct answer is D.

2. Explanation: There are four lines of triangles with 3 triangles in each line. So to find the total number of triangles, we should add 3 + 3 + 3 + 3, which equals 12. To check, count and you will see there are 12 triangles.

The correct answer is B.

3. Explanation: There are four lines of squares with 5 squares in each line. So to find the total number of squares, we should add 5 + 5 + 5 + 5, which equals 20. To check, count and you will see there are 20 squares.

The correct answer is A.

4. Explanation: There are two lines of stars with 6 stars in each line. So to find the total number of stars, we should add 6 + 6, which equals 12. To check, count and you will see there are 12 stars.

The correct answer is A.

5. Explanation: There are three lines of circles with 3 circles in each line. So to find the total number of circles, we should add 3 + 3 + 3, which equals 9. To check, count and you will see there are 9 circles.

The correct answer is C.

6. Explanation: There are two lines of stars with 5 stars in each line. So to find the total number of stars, we should add 5 + 5, which equals 10. To check, count and you will see there are 10 stars.

The correct answer is D.

7. Explanation: There are fours lines of hearts with **2** hearts in each line. So to find the total number of hearts, we should add **2 + 2 + 2 + 2**, which equals **8**. To check, count and you will see there are **8** hearts.

The correct answer is A.

8. Explanation: There are four lines of triangles with four triangles in each line. So to find the total number of triangles, we should add **4 + 4 + 4 + 4**, which equals **16**. To check, count and you will see there are **16** triangles.

The correct answer is B.

9. Explanation: There are three lines of rectangles with **5** rectangles in each line. So to find the total number of rectangles, we should add **5 + 5 + 5**, which equals **15**. To check, count and you will see there are **15** rectangles.

The correct answer is D.

10. Explanation: The problem **2 x 3**, can be illustrated by drawing **2** sets of **3** objects or **6** total objects.

The correct answer is D.

11. Explanation: The problem **4 x 1**, can be illustrated by drawing **4** sets of **1** object or **4** total objects.

The correct answer is B.

12. Explanation: The problem **5 x 6**, can be illustrated by drawing **5** sets of **6** objects or **30** total objects.

The correct answer is A.

13. Explanation: The problem **8 x 3**, can be illustrated by drawing **8** sets of **3** objects or **24** total objects.

The correct answer is A.

14. Explanation: The problem **2 x 9**, can be illustrated by drawing **2** sets of **9** objects or **18** total objects.

The correct answer is D.

15. Explanation: The problem **7 x 3**, can be illustrated by drawing **7** sets of **3** objects or **21** total objects.

The correct answer is A.

✳ Operations and Algebraic Thinking ✳
✳ Multiplication and Division ✳

1. Which set of objects illustrates the problem 2 x 5?

A.

B.

C.

D.

Difficulty: Hard

2. Which set of objects illustrates the problem 4 x 6?

A.

B.

C.

D.

Difficulty: Hard

3. Which set of objects illustrates the problem 9 x 8?

A.

B.

C.

D.

Difficulty: Hard

4. Which set of objects represents the problem 14 ÷ 2?

A.

B.

C.

D.

Difficulty: Hard

5. Which set of objects represents the problem 35 ÷ 7?

A.

B.

C.

D.

Difficulty: Hard

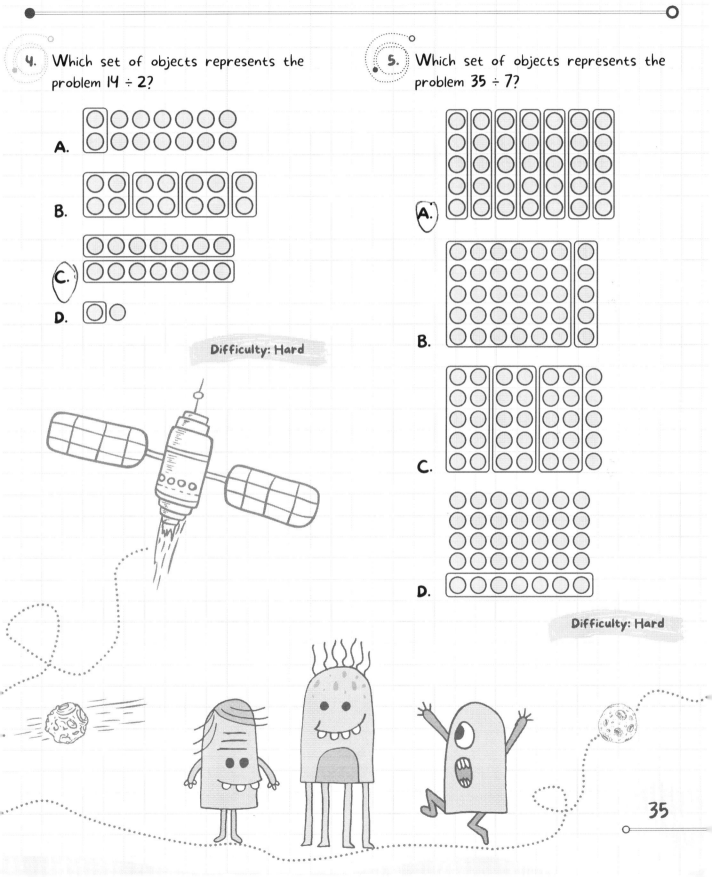

6. Which set of objects represents the problem 24 ÷ 4?

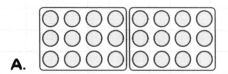

A.

B.

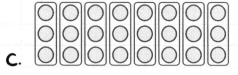

C.

D.

Difficulty: Hard

7. Which set of objects represents the problem 32 ÷ 8?

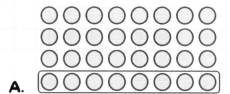

A.

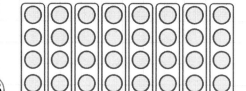

B.

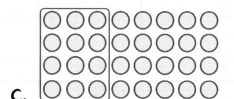

C.

D.

Difficulty: Hard

8. Which set of objects represents the problem 10 ÷ 5?

A.

B.

C.

D.

Difficulty: Hard

9. Which set of objects represents the problem 12 ÷ 3?

A.

B.

C.

D.

Difficulty: Hard

10. Which set of objects represents the problem 36 ÷ 9?

A.

B.

C.

D.

Difficulty: Hard

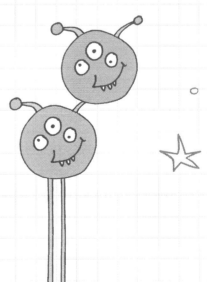

11. Which set of objects represents the problem **20 ÷ 4?**

A.

B.

C.

D.

Difficulty: Hard

12. Which set of objects represents the problem **36 ÷ 6?**

A.

B.

C.

D.

Difficulty: Hard

13. 5 x 7 =

   A. 20   C. 30

   B. 25   D. 35

Difficulty: Hard

14. 4 x 9 =

   A. 36   C. 32

   B. 40   D. 30

Difficulty: Hard

15. 3 x 6 =

   A. 15   C. 21

   B. 18   D. 24

Difficulty: Hard

16. 2 x 9 =

   A. 18   C. 22

   B. 20   D. 24

Difficulty: Hard

17. 4 x 4 =

   A. 12   C. 16

   B. 14   D. 18

Difficulty: Hard

18. 4 x 3 =

   A. 18   C. 14

   B. 16   D. 12

Difficulty: Hard

19. 8 x 2 =

   A. 14   C. 18

   B. 16   D. 20

Difficulty: Hard

20. 9 x 7 =

   A. 54   C. 72

   B. 63   D. 81

Difficulty: Hard

21. 3 x 5 =

   A. 15   C. 17

   B. 16   D. 18

Difficulty: Hard

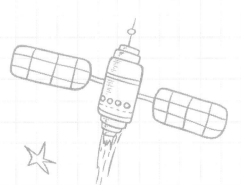

1. Explanation: The problem **2 x 5**, can be illustrated by drawing **2** sets of **5** objects or **10** total objects.

   The correct answer is C.

2. Explanation: The problem **4 x 6**, can be illustrated by drawing **4** sets of **6** objects or **24** total objects.

   The correct answer is B.

3. Explanation: The problem **9 x 8**, can be illustrated by drawing **9** sets of **8** objects or **72** total objects.

   The correct answer is B.

4. Explanation: The problem **14 ÷ 2**, can be illustrated by splitting **14** into **2** equal sets of **7** each.

   The correct answer is C.

5. Explanation: The problem **35 ÷ 7**, can be illustrated by splitting **35** into **7** equal sets of **5** each.

   The correct answer is A.

6. Explanation: The problem **24 ÷ 4**, can be illustrated by splitting **24** into **4** equal sets of **6** each.

   The correct answer is B.

7. Explanation: The problem **32 ÷ 8**, can be illustrated by splitting **32** into **8** equal sets of **4** each.

   The correct answer is B.

8. Explanation: The problem **10 ÷ 5**, can be illustrated by splitting **10** into **5** equal sets of **2** each.

   The correct answer is C.

9. Explanation: The problem **12 ÷ 3**, can be illustrated by splitting **12** into **3** equal sets of **4** each.

   The correct answer is C.

10. Explanation: The problem **36 ÷ 9**, can be illustrated by splitting **36** into **9** equal sets of **4** each.

    The correct answer is C.

11. Explanation: The problem $20 ÷ 4$, can be illustrated by splitting 20 into 4 equal sets of 5 each.

    The correct answer is B.

12. Explanation: The problem $36 ÷ 6$, can be illustrated by splitting 36 into 6 equal sets of 6 each.

    The correct answer is A.

13. Explanation: This problem is solved by 5 sets of 7 or 35.

    The correct answer is D.

14. Explanation: This problem is solved by 4 sets of 9 or 36.

    The correct answer is A.

15. Explanation: This problem is solved by 3 sets of 6 or 18.

    The correct answer is B.

16. Explanation: This problem is solved by 2 sets of 9 or 18.

    The correct answer is A.

17. Explanation: This problem is solved by 4 sets of 4 or 16.

    The correct answer is C.

18. Explanation: This problem is solved by 4 sets of 3 or 12.

    The correct answer is D.

19. Explanation: This problem is solved by 8 sets of 2 or 16.

    The correct answer is B.

20. Explanation: This problem is solved by 9 sets of 7 or 63.

    The correct answer is B.

21. Explanation: This problem is solved by 3 sets of 5 or 15.

    The correct answer is A.

1. 18 ÷ 2 =

A. 6   C. 8
B. 7   D. 9

Difficulty: Hard

2. 49 ÷ 7 =

A. 5   C. 7
B. 6   D. 8

Difficulty: Hard

3. 48 ÷ 6 =

A. 5   C. 7
B. 6   D. 8

Difficulty: Hard

4. 27 ÷ 3 =

A. 9   C. 7
B. 8   D. 6

Difficulty: Hard

5. 64 ÷ 8 =

A. 5   C. 7
B. 6   D. 8

Difficulty: Hard

6. 28 ÷ 4 =

A. 5   C. 7
B. 6   D. 8

Difficulty: Hard

7. 54 ÷ 9 =

A. 5   C. 7
B. 6   D. 8

Difficulty: Hard

8. 35 ÷ 5 =

A. 5   C. 7
B. 6   D. 8

Difficulty: Hard

9. ? × 4 = 16

A. 4   C. 6
B. 5   D. 7

Difficulty: Hard

10. ? ÷ 3 = 4

A. 12   C. 16
B. 14   D. 18

Difficulty: Hard

11. 8 x ? = 56

A. 5　　　C. 7

B. 6　　　D. 8

Difficulty: Hard

16. ? ÷ 2 = 10

A. 16　　　C. 20

B. 18　　　D. 22

Difficulty: Hard

12. 42 ÷ ? = 6

A. 8　　　C. 6

B. 7　　　D. 5

Difficulty: Hard

17. 18 ÷ ? = 3

A. 6　　　C. 8

B. 7　　　D. 9

Difficulty: Hard

13. ? x 5 = 40

A. 5　　　C. 7

B. 6　　　D. 8

Difficulty: Hard

18. Which problem is the same as 4 x 3?

A. 4 + 3　　　C. 3 x 4

B. 3 x 3　　　D. 4 x 4

Difficulty: Hard

14. 5 x ? = 25

A. 4　　　C. 6

B. 5　　　D. 7

Difficulty: Hard

19. Which problem is the same as 7 x 5?

A. 7 + 5　　　C. 5 x 7

B. 7 x 7　　　D. 5 x 5

Difficulty: Hard

15. ? ÷ 7 = 2

A. 14　　　C. 18

B. 16　　　D. 20

Difficulty: Hard

20. Which problem is the same as 2 x 9?

A. 9 x 2　　　C. 2 x 2

B. 9 x 9　　　D. 9 + 2

Difficulty: Hard

1. Explanation: This problem is solved by dividing 18 into 2 sets of 9.

   The correct answer is D.

2. Explanation: This problem is solved by dividing 49 into 7 sets of 7.

   The correct answer is C.

3. Explanation: This problem is solved by dividing 48 into 6 sets of 8.

   The correct answer is D.

4. Explanation: This problem is solved by dividing 27 into 3 sets of 9.

   The correct answer is A.

5. Explanation: This problem is solved by dividing 64 into 8 sets of 8.

   The correct answer is D.

6. Explanation: This problem is solved by dividing 28 into 4 sets of 7.

   The correct answer is C.

7. Explanation: This problem is solved by dividing 54 into 9 sets of 6.

   The correct answer is B.

8. Explanation: This problem is solved by dividing 35 into 5 sets of 7.

   The correct answer is C.

9. Explanation: $4 \times 4 = 16$

   The correct answer is A.

10. Explanation: $12 \div 3 = 4$

    The correct answer is A.

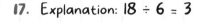
11. Explanation: 8 x 7 = 56

The correct answer is C.

12. Explanation: 42 ÷ 7 = 6

The correct answer is B.

13. Explanation: 8 x 5 = 40

The correct answer is D.

14. Explanation: 5 x 5 = 25

The correct answer is B.

15. Explanation: 14 ÷ 7 = 2

The correct answer is A.

16. Explanation: 20 ÷ 2 = 10

The correct answer is C.

17. Explanation: 18 ÷ 6 = 3

The correct answer is A.

18. Explanation: Order does not matter when you multiply. 4 x 3 is the same as 3 x 4, both give you 12.

The correct answer is C.

19. Explanation: Order does not matter when you multiply. 5 x7 is the same as 7 x 5, both give you 35.

The correct answer is C.

20. Explanation: Order does not matter when you multiply. 2 x 9 is the same as 9 x 2, both give you 18.

The correct answer is A.

1. Which problem is the same as 6 x 8?

A. 8 x 8   C. 6 x 6
B. 8 x 6   D. 8 + 6

Difficulty: Hard

2. Which problem is the same as 10 x 2?

A. 10 + 2   C. 2 x 2
B. 10 x 10   D. 2 x 10

Difficulty: Hard

3. Which problem is the same as 5 x 9?

A. 9 x 5   C. 9 - 5
B. 9 + 5   D. 5 + 9

Difficulty: Hard

4. Which problem is the same as 3 x 7?

A. 3 x 3   C. 7 x 7
B. 7 x 3   D. 3 + 7

Difficulty: Hard

5. Which problem is the same as 8 x 4?

A. 8 + 8   C. 4 x 8
B. 8 + 4   D. 4 + 4

Difficulty: Hard

6. Which problem is the same as 2 x 6?

A. 2 + 6   C. 6 x 2
B. 6 + 6   D. 2 + 2

Difficulty: Hard

7. What will give you an even sum?

A. Multiplying by 2
B. Multiplying by 3
C. Multiplying by 5
D. Multiplying by 7

Difficulty: Hard

8. What problem will give you an odd sum?

A. 6 + 6   C. 6 x 6
B. 3 x 3   D. 3 x 6

Difficulty: Hard

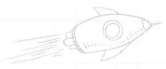

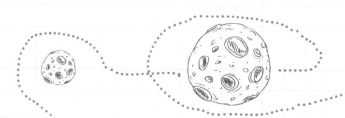

9. What is the pattern? 3, 5, 7, 9, 11

   A. × 2   **C.** + 3

   B. + 2   **D.** + 1

Difficulty: Hard

10. What is the pattern? 3, 6, 12, 24, 48

   A. × 4   **C.** × 2

   B. + 6   **D.** + 2

Difficulty: Hard

11. What is the pattern? 2, 10, 50, 250

   A. + 10   **C.** + 5

   B. × 2   **D.** × 5

Difficulty: Hard

12. What is the pattern? 1, 4, 7, 10

   A. + 3   **C.** - 3

   B. × 3   **D.** + 6

Difficulty: Hard

13. What is the pattern? 38, 32, 26, 20

   A. + 6   **C.** × 6

   B. - 6   **D.** ÷ 6

Difficulty: Hard

14. What is the pattern? 80, 40, 20, 10

   A. × 2   **C.** + 2

   B. ÷ 2   **D.** - 20

Difficulty: Hard

15. What is the pattern? 62, 55, 48, 41

   A. + 14   **C.** + 7

   B. × 7   **D.** - 7

Difficulty: Hard

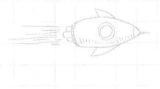

1. Explanation: Order does not matter when you multiply. 6 x 8 is the same as 8 x 6, both give you 48.

   The correct answer is B.

2. Explanation: Order does not matter when you multiply. 10 x 2 is the same as 2 x 10, both give you 20.

   The correct answer is D.

3. Explanation: Order does not matter when you multiply. 5 x 9 is the same as 9 x 5, both give you 45.

   The correct answer is A.

4. Explanation: Order does not matter when you multiply. 3 x 7 is the same as 7 x 3, both give you 21.

   The correct answer is B.

5. Explanation: Order does not matter when you multiply. 8 x 4 is the same as 4 x 8, both give you 32.

   The correct answer is C.

6. Explanation: Order does not matter when you multiply. 2 x 6 is the same as 6 x 2, both give you 12.

   The correct answer is C.

7. Explanation: Even numbers are divisible by 2. Multiplying any number by 2 will make it even because it is now divisible by 2.

   The correct answer is A.

8. Explanation: Odd numbers are not divisible by 2. Choice A is 12, choice B is 9, choice C is 36, and choice D is 18. The only number not divisible by 2 is 9.

   The correct answer is B.

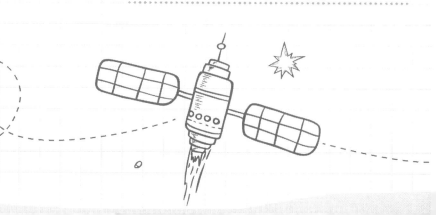

9. Explanation: Each number is **2** more than the number before it, so the pattern is + **2**.

   The correct answer is B.

10. Explanation: Each number is double the number before it, so the pattern is x **2**.

    The correct answer is C.

11. Explanation: Each number is **5** times the number before it, so the pattern is x **5**.

    The correct answer is D.

12. Explanation: Each number is **3** more than the number before it, so the pattern is + **3**.

    The correct answer is A.

13. Explanation: Each number is **6** less than the number before it, so the pattern is - **6**.

    The correct answer is B.

14. Explanation: Each number is $\frac{1}{2}$ the number before it, so the pattern is ÷ **2**.

    The correct answer is B.

15. Explanation: Each number is **7** less than the number for it, so the pattern is -**7**.

    The correct answer is D.

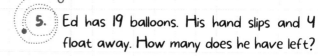
1. Elizabeth has 4 crayons and Mary has 6 crayons. How many crayons do they have together?

A. 8   C. 12

B. 10   D. 14

Difficulty: Easy

2. Martin has 10 cars. He gives 3 cars to his brother. How many cars does he have left?

A. 3   C. 7

B. 5   D. 9

Difficulty: Easy

3. Amanda has 2 paintings. She paints 5 more. How many paintings does she have now?

A. 7   C. 9

B. 8   D. 10

Difficulty: Easy

4. Chris has 4 cupcakes. He gives one to his mom and one to his dad. How many cupcakes does he have left?

A. 8   C. 4

B. 6   D. 2

Difficulty: Easy

5. Ed has 19 balloons. His hand slips and 4 float away. How many does he have left?

A. 13   C. 15

B. 14   D. 16

Difficulty: Easy

6. Missy has 7 stuffed bears. She receives 4 more for her birthday. How many bears does she have now?

A. 9   C. 13

B. 11   D. 15

Difficulty: Easy

7. Sean picks 6 flowers for his mom. He goes to another garden and picks 8 more flowers. How many flowers does he have total to give to his mom?

A. 8   C. 12

B. 10   D. 14

Difficulty: Easy

8. Ashley read 11 books last week and 4 more books this week. How many books does she read this week?

A. 15   C. 19

B. 17   D. 21

Difficulty: Easy

9. We bought 12 eggs at the store last week and used 8 to make dinner. How many eggs do we have left?

A. 7   C. 5

B. 6   D. 4

Difficulty: Easy

10. Fido saved 3 bones last week and 1 bone this week. How many bones does he have in all?

A. 3   C. 5

B. 4   D. 6

Difficulty: Easy

11. There are 34 students in our class. Six students go to another teacher for math. How many students are in our class for math?

A. 28   C. 32

B. 30   D. 34

Difficulty: Medium

12. Alicia collects pennies. She has 56 pennies in her collection. Her mom gives her 36 more pennies. How many pennies does Alicia have now?

A. 92   C. 72

B. 82   D. 62

Difficulty: Medium

13. Manuel mows lawns to earn money. Last week he earned $34. He spent $17 at a movie over the weekend. How much money does he have this week?

A. $7   C. $17

B. $20   D. $51

Difficulty: Medium

14. Elizabeth has 16 girl scout badges. She plans to earn 6 more over this year. How many badges will she have at the end of this year?

A. 10   C. 32

B. 22   D. 15

Difficulty: Medium

1. Explanation: To solve this problem, you need to add the crayons together. $4 + 6 = 10$

   The correct answer is B.

2. Explanation: To solve this problem, you need to subtract what he gives away from the total amount. $10 - 3 = 7$

   The correct answer is C.

3. Explanation: To solve this problem, you need to add the paintings together. $2 + 5 = 7$

   The correct answer is A.

4. Explanation: To solve this problem, you need to subtract two (one for each parent) from the original amount. $4 - 2 = 2$

   The correct answer is D.

5. Explanation: To solve this problem, you need to subtract the number that float away from the original amount. $19 - 4 = 15$

   The correct answer is C.

6. Explanation: To solve this problem, you need to add the two amounts together. $7 + 4 = 11$

   The correct answer is B.

7. Explanation: To solve this problem, you need to add the two amounts together. $6 + 8 = 14$

   The correct answer is D.

8. Explanation: To solve this problem, you need to add 4 more to the amount of books she read last week. $4 + 11 = 15$

   The correct answer is A.

9. Explanation: To solve this problem, we need to take 12 - 8, which is 4.

The correct answer is D.

10. Explanation: To solve this problem, we need to take 3 + 1, which is 4.

The correct answer is B.

11. Explanation: To solve this problem, you take the total students minus the ones who leave, or 34 - 6, which gives you 28.

The correct answer is A.

12. Explanation: To solve this problem, you take the number of pennies Alicia started with and add the pennies her mom gave her, or 56 + 36, which gives you 92.

The correct answer is A.

13. Explanation: To solve this problem, you take the total he earned and subtract what he spent, or 34 - 17, which gives you 17.

The correct answer is C.

14. Explanation: To solve this problem, you need to add what she currently has plus what she wants to earn, or 16 + 6, which equals 22.

The correct answer is B.

1. Jose has 17 boy scout merit badges. He earned 7 over this past year. How many badges did he earn last year?

A. 16   C. 12

B. 14   D. 10

Difficulty: Medium

2. Marie has 74 pages left in her book to read. If she reads 34 pages tonight, how many pages does she have left to read tomorrow?

A. 40   C. 60

B. 50   D. 70

Difficulty: Medium

3. There are 28 students in our class. Our class received donations for 16 computers. How many more computers do we need for each student to have a computer?

A. 10   C. 12

B. 16   D. 14

Difficulty: Medium

4. Jonathan has a collection of cars. He has 14 cars and he receives 9 more for his birthday. How many cars does he have now?

A. 22   C. 24

B. 23   D. 25

Difficulty: Medium

5. Last week, our class earned 42 minutes of extra recess. We got in trouble and lost 12 minutes of it. How much extra recess do we have left?

A. 18   C. 22

B. 30   D. 24

Difficulty: Medium

6. Last month it rained 15 days. If it rained 6 days less this month, how many days did it rain this month?

A. 9   C. 7

B. 8   D. 6

Difficulty: Medium

7. There are 16 horses in our stable. Each stall holds 2 horses. How many stalls do we need to house our horses?

A. 8   C. 4

B. 6   D. 2

Difficulty: Hard

8. There are four spiders on my porch. Each spider has 8 legs. How many spider legs are on my porch?

A. 28   C. 32

B. 30   D. 34

Difficulty: Hard

9. Our teacher brought in pencils for some kids in our class. If she wanted each kid to have 3 pencils and she brought in 27 pencils, how many kids were going to get new pencils?

A. 8   C. 10

B. 9   D. 11

Difficulty: Hard

10. We worked on math problems for homework last night. We were practicing 2 different topics and did 10 problems on each topic. How many total problems did we do?

A. 14   C. 18

B. 16   D. 20

Difficulty: Hard

11. Mario practiced his piano for 60 minutes. If he practiced 5 songs, how many minutes did he practice each song?

A. 12   C. 10

B. 11   D. 9

Difficulty: Hard

12. A train has 6 cars. Each car holds 11 people. How many people can ride on the train?

A. 56   C. 66

B. 54   D. 60

Difficulty: Hard

1. Explanation: To solve this problem, we take the badges he has and subtract 7 to see how many he earned last year, or 17-7, which equals 10.

   The correct answer is D.

2. Explanation: To solve this problem, you take the pages she has left and subtract the pages she has read, 74 - 34, which equals 40.

   The correct answer is A.

3. Explanation: To solve this problem, you take the total number of students and subtract the number of computers, 28 - 16, which equals 12.

   The correct answer is C.

4. Explanation: To solve this problem, you add the cars together. 14 + 9 equals 23.

   The correct answer is B.

5. Explanation: To solve this problem, you subtract what you lost from the original amount. 42 - 12 = 30

   The correct answer is B.

6. Explanation: To solve this problem, you subtract 6 from 15. 15 - 6 = 9

   The correct answer is A.

7. Explanation: To solve this problem, you need to divide the number of horses by the number of stalls. 16 ÷ 2 = 8

   The correct answer is A.

8. Explanation: To solve this problem, you need to multiply the number of spiders by the number of legs. 4 x 8 = 32

   The correct answer is C.

9. Explanation: To solve this problem, you need to divide the total number pencils by the number of pencils per kid. 27 ÷ 3 = 9

   The correct answer is B.

10. Explanation: To solve this problem, you multiply the number of topics by the number of problems. 10 x 2 = 20

    The correct answer is D.

11. Explanation: To solve this problem, you divide the number of minutes by the number of songs. 60 ÷ 5 = 12

    The correct answer is A.

12. Explanation: To solve this problem, you multiply the number of people by the number of cars. 11 x 6 = 66

    The correct answer is C.

1. For lunch one day, a school serves **12** salads, **32** sandwiches and **63** hot lunches. Estimate, how many total entrees do they serve?

A. 110   C. 100

B. 120   D. 130

Difficulty: Hard

2. The temperature in the morning was **76°F**. It cooled off to **63°F** by 2 PM. That afternoon, it warmed up to **68°F**. What was the total change in temperature?

A. 8°   C. 13°

B. 5°   D. 18°

Difficulty: Hard

3. This month, we found **4** frogs, **3** fish, and **2** turtles in our stream. Which problem represents the total number of animals we found in our stream?

A. 4 x 3 x 2   C. 4 - 3 - 2

B. 4 + 3 + 2   D. 4 ÷ 3 ÷ 2

Difficulty: Hard

4. I need $45 for a video game. I received $20 for my birthday and earned another $5. Which problem will help me determine how much money I still need to save?

A. 20 + 5   C. 25 + 5

B. 15 + 5   D. 45 + 5

Difficulty: Hard

5. Our reading assignment is a book of **110** pages. I have already read **60** pages. If I plan to read **10** pages each day, how many days will it take me to finish the book?

A. 3   C. 5

B. 4   D. 6

Difficulty: Hard

6. Andre scored **11** points during his first basketball game. At his next game, he scored **5** more points. If he scored **39** points in three games, how many points did he score in the third game?

A. 10   C. 11

B. 12   D. 16

Difficulty: Hard

7. Our class has **32** students. If there are **8** tables in our room, how many students can sit at each table?

A. 4   C. 6

B. 5   D. 7

Difficulty: Hard

8. Last week, our class read **32** books. This week, we read **26** books. If we read **22** books next week, how many books will we have read over the three weeks?

A. 30   C. 50

B. 40   D. 80

Difficulty: Hard

9. Owen walked **6** blocks to school in the morning. After school, he walked **6** blocks home and then he walked **4** blocks to his friend's house. How far did he walk?

A. 10   C. 11

B. 12   D. 16

Difficulty: Hard

10. Natalie is saving for **2** toys, one that costs **$32** and one that costs **$26**. If she receives **$60** for her birthday, will she have enough for both toys? Explain your response.

Difficulty: Hard

11. Rose is reading a book with **9** chapters. If it takes her **2** days to read a chapter, how many days will it take her to read the whole book?

A. 14   C. 18

B. 16   D. 20

Difficulty: Hard

12. Marta's mom buys water bottles for our soccer practice. If the bottles come in packs of 10, and there are 24 kids on our team, how many packs of bottles does she need to buy? Explain your answer.

Difficulty: Hard

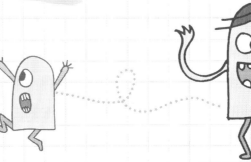

1. Explanation: To solve, you should round each entrée to the nearest 10. You should add 10 + 30 + 60, you will get 100.

   The correct answer is C.

2. Explanation: First you take 76 - 63, which equals 13. Then you take 68 - 63, which equals 5. Then you add 13 and 5, which equals 18.

   The correct answer is D.

3. Explanation: To find the answer, you need to add each type of animal.

   The correct answer is B.

4. Explanation: To find the answer, you need to figure out how much money you already have, which is your birthday money and the money you earned.

   The correct answer is A.

5. Explanation: To solve, first you need to subtract 110 - 60. Then you take 50 and divide by 10, to figure how many days it will take to read.

   The correct answer is C.

6. Explanation: First, you figure how much he scored in the second game (11 + 5). Then you need to add the first game and the second game together, 11 + 16 = 27. Then you subtract that amount from the total amount 39 - 27, which equals 12.

   The correct answer is B.

7. Explanation: To solve, you need to divide the number of students by the number of tables. 32 ÷ 4 = 8

   The correct answer is A.

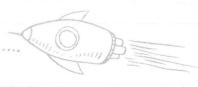

8. Explanation: To solve this problem, you need to combine the three amounts. 32 + 26 + 22 = 80

   The correct answer is D.

9. Explanation: To solve this problem, you add 6 + 6 + 4, which is 16 blocks.

   The correct answer is D.

10. Explanation: 32 + 26 = 58, which is smaller than 60 so yes, she has enough money for both toys.

    The correct answer is Yes. Students should include an explanation that includes the total amount of money she needs to spend.

11. Explanation: To solve the problem, you take 9 x 2, which is 18.

    The correct answer is C.

12. Explanation: If she needs at least 24 bottles, she needs to buy 3 packs. If she bought 2 packs, that would not provide enough for everyone.

    The correct answer is 3. Students should include an explanation of how because 20 is less than 24, her mom needs to buy at least 30.

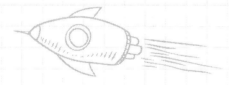

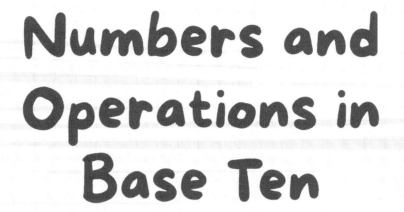

Numbers and Operations in Base Ten

1. Counting page 64

2. **Number Forms** page 70

3. Rounding page 72

4. **Number Sense and Place Value** page 74

5. Compare by looking at 100, 10, 1s (<, >, =) page 88

6. **Using place value to perform operations** page 90

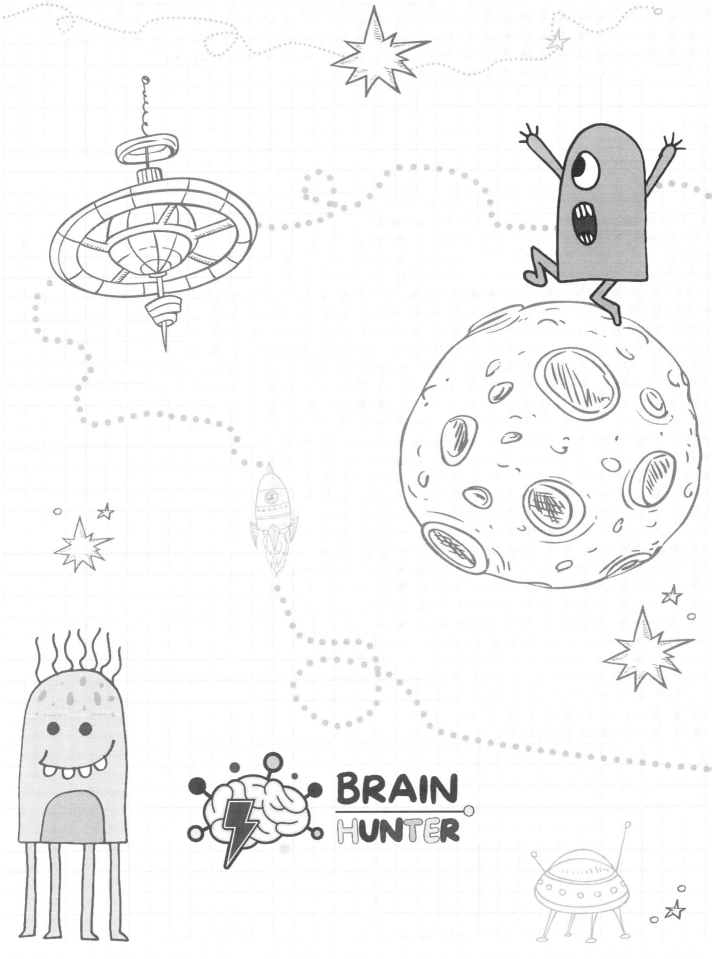

1. Which number is the next in the following sequence?

88, 89, 90, _____

A. 87   C. 92
B. 91   D. 95

Difficulty: Easy

2. Which number is the next in the following sequence?

104, 105, 106, _____

A. 107   C. 109
B. 108   D. 110

Difficulty: Easy

3. Which number is the next in the following sequence?

32, 33, 34, 35, _____

A. 36   C. 40
B. 38   D. 41

Difficulty: Easy

4. Which number completes the following sequence?

_____, 98, 99, 100, 101

A. 93   C. 97
B. 105   D. 102

Difficulty: Easy

5. Which number completes the following sequence?

63, 64, _____, 66, 67

A. 62   C. 64
B. 63   D. 65

Difficulty: Easy

6. Which number completes the following sequence?

49, _____, 51, 52

A. 48   C. 52
B. 50   D. 53

Difficulty: Easy

7. Which number completes the following sequence?

_____, 72, 73, 74

A. 71   C. 75
B. 70   D. 80

Difficulty: Easy

8. Which number completes the following sequence?

402, 403, 404, _____

A. 402   C. 404
B. 403   D. 405

Difficulty: Medium

9. Which number completes the following sequence?

772, 773, _____, 775

A. 774   C. 776

B. 775   D. 777

Difficulty: Medium

10. Which number completes the following sequence?

599, 600, _____, 602

A. 600   C. 603

B. 601   D. 604

Difficulty: Medium

11. Which number completes the following sequence?

_____, 480, 481, 482

A. 459   C. 479

B. 469   D. 489

Difficulty: Medium

12. Which number completes the following sequence?

319, _____, 321, 322

A. 320   C. 310

B. 330   D. 340

Difficulty: Medium

13. Which number completes the following sequence?

246, 247, 248, _____

A. 246   C. 249

B. 248   D. 250

Difficulty: Medium

14. Which number completes the following sequence?

819, _____, 821, 822

A. 825   C. 818

B. 823   D. 820

Difficulty: Medium

15. Which number completes the following sequence?

20, 25, _____, 35

A. 10   C. 30

B. 20   D. 40

Difficulty: Medium

16. Which number completes the following sequence?

30, 40, 50, _____

A. 60   C. 80

B. 70   D. 90

Difficulty: Medium

1. Explanation: When you count, the sequence is as follows: 88, 89, 90, 91.

   The correct answer is B.

2. Explanation: When you count, the sequence is as follows: 104, 105, 106, 107.

   The correct answer is A.

3. Explanation: When you count, the sequence is as follows: 32, 33, 34, 35, 36.

   The correct answer is A.

4. Explanation: When you count, the sequence is as follows: 97, 98, 99, 100, 101.

   The correct answer is C.

5. Explanation: When you count, the sequence is as follows: 63, 64, 65, 66, 67.

   The correct answer is D.

6. Explanation: When you count, the sequence is as follows: 49, 50, 51, 52.

   The correct answer is B.

7. Explanation: When you count, the sequence is as follows: 71, 72, 73, 74.

   The correct answer is A.

8. Explanation: When you count, the sequence is as follows: 402, 403, 404, 405.

   The correct answer is D.

9. Explanation: When you count, the sequence is as follows: 772, 773, 774, 775.

   The correct answer is A.

10. Explanation: When you count, the sequence is as follows: 599, 600, 601, 602.

    The correct answer is B.

11. Explanation: When you count, the sequence is as follows: 479, 480, 481, 482.

The correct answer is C.

12. Explanation: When you count, the sequence is as follows: 319, 320, 321, 322.

The correct answer is A.

13. Explanation: When you count, the sequence is as follows: 246, 247, 248, 249.

The correct answer is C.

14. Explanation: When you count, the sequence is as follows: 819, 820, 821, 822.

The correct answer is D.

15. Explanation: When you count, the sequence is as follows: 20, 25, 30, 35.

The correct answer is C.

16. Explanation: When you count, the sequence is as follows: 30, 40, 50, 60.

The correct answer is A.

✳ Numbers and Operations in Base Ten ✳
✳ Counting ✳

1. Which number completes the following sequence?

_____ , 600, 700, 800

A. 400   C. 600

B. 500   D. 700

Difficulty: Medium

2. Which number completes the following sequence?

100, _____, 300, 400.

A. 500   C. 300

B. 400   D. 200

Difficulty: Medium

3. Which number completes the following sequence?

65, 70, _____, 80

A. 75   C. 85

B. 80   D. 90

Difficulty: Medium

4. Which number completes the following sequence?

310, 320, _____, 340

A. 300   C. 330

B. 350   D. 325

Difficulty: Medium

5. Which number completes the following sequence?

890, _____, 910, 920

A. 900   C. 930

B. 901   D. 880

Difficulty: Medium

1. Explanation: When you count, the sequence is as follows: 500, 600, 700, 800.

   The correct answer is B.

2. Explanation: When you count, the sequence is as follows: 100, 200, 300, 400.

   The correct answer is D.

3. Explanation: When you count, the sequence is as follows: 65, 70, 75, 80.

   The correct answer is A.

4. Explanation: When you count, the sequence is as follows: 310, 320, 330, 340.

   The correct answer is C.

5. Explanation: When you count, the sequence is as follows: 890, 900, 910, 920.

   The correct answer is A.

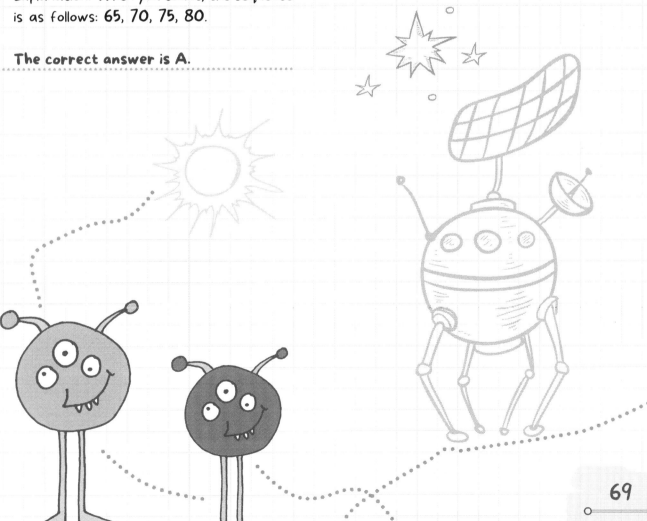

1. Which number is equal to 932?

   A. 900 + 20 + 3
   B. 200 + 30 + 9
   C. 900 + 30 + 2
   D. 300 + 90 + 2

Difficulty: Medium

2. Which number is equal to 46?

   A. Sixty-four   **C.** Four six
   B. Forty-six   **D.** Six four

Difficulty: Medium

3. Which number is equal to 500 + 30 + 7?

   A. 573   **C.** 357
   B. 735   **D.** 537

Difficulty: Medium

4. Which number is equal to ninety-five?

   A. 90 + 5   **C.** 9 + 5
   B. 50 + 9   **D.** 50 + 40

Difficulty: Medium

5. Which number is equal to eight hundred fifty- three?

   A. 853   **C.** 883
   B. 583   **D.** 358

Difficulty: Medium

6. Which number is equal to 600+ 7?

   A. 670   **C.** 617
   B. 607   **D.** 677

Difficulty: Medium

7. Which number is equal to 890?

   A. Eight hundred nine
   B. Eight hundred ninety-nine
   C. Eight hundred ninety
   D. Eight hundred and nine

Difficulty: Medium

1. Explanation: When you write 932 in expanded form, the correct format is 900 + 30 + 2 as you have 9 hundreds, 3 tens, and 2 ones.

   The correct answer is C.

2. Explanation: When you write forty-six in numbers, you need to designate the 4 is forty not four.

   The correct answer is B.

3. Explanation: When you write 500+30+7 in base 10 form, the correct order of numerals is 537.

   The correct answer is D.

4. Explanation: When you write ninety-five in expanded form, the correct format is 90 +5 as you have 9 tens and 5 ones.

   The correct answer is A.

5. Explanation: When you write eight hundred fifty- three in base ten form, the correct order is 853.

   The correct answer is A.

6. Explanation: When you write 600+7 in base ten form, the correct order of numerals is 607.

   The correct answer is B.

7. Explanation, when you write 890 in words, you need to designate the 9 as ninety not nine.

   The correct answer is C.

1. Round to the nearest 10: 87

    A. 70   **C.** 90

    B. 80   **D.** 100

Difficulty: Hard

2. Round to the nearest 10: 634

    A. 600   **C.** 640

    B. 630   **D.** 700

Difficulty: Hard

3. Round to the nearest 10: 993

    A. 1010   **C.** 1000

    B. 980   **D.** 990

Difficulty: Hard

4. Round to the nearest 100: 583

    A. 600   **C.** 700

    B. 500   **D.** 400

Difficulty: Hard

5. Round to the nearest 100: 791

    A. 1000   **C.** 800

    B. 900   **D.** 700

Difficulty: Hard

6. Round to the nearest 10: 728

    A. 740   **C.** 730

    B. 720   **D.** 710

Difficulty: Hard

7. Round to the nearest 100: 226

    A. 200   **C.** 220

    B. 300   **D.** 230

Difficulty: Hard

1. Explanation: To round to the nearest ten, you look at the ones place. 7 rounds the 8 up to 9.

   The correct answer is C.

2. Explanation: To round to the nearest ten, you look at the ones place. 4 keeps the 3 at 3.

   The correct answer is B.

3. Explanation: To round to the nearest ten, you look at the ones place. 3 keeps the 9 at 9.

   The correct answer is D.

4. Explanation: To round to the nearest hundred, you look at the tens place. 8 rounds the 5 up to 6.

   The correct answer is A.

5. Explanation: To round to the nearest hundred, you look at the tens place. 9 rounds the 7 up to 8.

   The correct answer is C.

6. Explanation: To round to the nearest ten, you look at the ones place. 8 rounds the 2 up to 3.

   The correct answer is C.

7. Explanation: To round to the nearest hundred, you look at the tens place. 2 keeps the 2 at 2.

   The correct answer is A.

1. Circle ten objects.

Difficulty: Easy

2. Circle ten objects.

Difficulty: Easy

3. Circle two groups of ten.

Difficulty: Easy

4. Circle two groups of ten.

Difficulty: Easy

5. Circle two groups of ten.

Difficulty: Easy

6. Draw 14 shapes and circle 10.

Difficulty: Easy

7. Is it possible to circle 10 from this group? Explain your answer.

Difficulty: Easy

8. Is it possible to circle 10 from this group? Explain your answer.

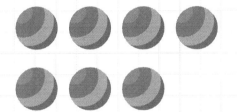

Difficulty: Easy

9. Which number is represented by the following tallies?

A. 11   C. 13

B. 12   D. 14

Difficulty: Easy

10. Which number is represented by the following tallies?

A. 14   C. 16

B. 15   D. 17

Difficulty: Easy

11. Which number is represented by the following tallies?

A. 12   C. 14

B. 13   D. 15

Difficulty: Easy

12. Which number is represented by the following tallies?

A. 17   C. 19

B. 18   D. 20

Difficulty: Easy

75

1. Explanation: You should count objects as you circle. Count the objects you have circled to check that you circled the right amount: 1, 2, 3, 4, 5, 6, 7, 8, 9, 10.

   Correct answer: Students should have circled 10 objects, leaving 6 uncircled.

2. Explanation: You should count objects as you circle. Count the objects you have circled to check that you circled the right amount: 1, 2, 3, 4, 5, 6, 7, 8, 9, 10.

   Correct answer: Students should have circled 10 objects, leaving 11 uncircled.

3. Explanation: You should count objects as you circle. Circle ten objects by counting to ten as you circle: 1, 2, 3, 4, 5, 6, 7, 8, 9, 10. Then, you should be able to circle another group of ten. Count as your circle another group: 1, 2, 3, 4, 5, 6, 7, 8, 9, 10.

   Correct answer: Students should have circled two groups, with ten objects in each group.

4. Explanation: You should count objects as you circle. Circle ten objects by counting to ten as you circle: 1, 2, 3, 4, 5, 6, 7, 8, 9, 10. Then, you should be able to circle another group of ten. Count as your circle another group: 1, 2, 3, 4, 5, 6, 7, 8, 9, 10.

   Correct answer: Students should have circled two groups, with ten objects in each group.

5. Explanation: You should count objects as you circle. Circle ten objects by counting to ten as you circle: 1, 2, 3, 4, 5, 6, 7, 8, 9, 10. Then, you should be able to circle another group of ten. Count as your circle another group: 1, 2, 3, 4, 5, 6, 7, 8, 9, 10. You should have 2 objects left over when you circle your two groups of 10.

   Correct answer: Students should have circled two groups, with ten objects in each group. Students should have two objects left over.

6. Explanation: You should count objects as you draw and as you circle. Count the objects you have drawn to be sure you drew the correct amount: 1, 2, 3, 4, 5, 6, 7, 8, 9, 10, 11, 12, 13, 14. Count the objects you have circled to check that you circled the right amount: 1, 2, 3, 4, 5, 6, 7, 8, 9, 10.

   Correct answer: Students should draw 14 shapes and circle 10 and leave 4 uncircled.

7. Explanation: You should count the objects as you circle. When you circle, you should count: 1, 2, 3, 4, 5, 6, 7, 8, 9, 10. You will have 12 objects left over after you circle 10.

   The correct answer is Yes. One possible explanation is I can circle and count 10.

8. Explanation: You should count objects as you try to circle. When I count, I only get to 7, which is smaller than 10, so I cannot circle 10 objects.

   The correct answer is No. One possible explanation is I cannot circle and count 10 objects because there are less than 10 objects.

9. Explanation: 13 is correct because 13 is a bundle of 10 and three ones.

   The correct answer is C.

10. Explanation: 16 is correct because 16 is a bundle of 10 and six ones.

    The correct answer is C.

11. Explanation: 12 is correct because 12 is a bundle of 10 and two ones.

    The correct answer is A.

12. Explanation: 19 is correct because 19 is a bundle of 10 and nine ones.

    The correct answer is C.

1. Which number is represented by the following tallies?

A. 14   C. 16
B. 15   D. 17

Difficulty: Easy

2. Which number is represented by the following tallies?

A. 11   C. 16
B. 14   D. 15

Difficulty: Easy

3. Which number is represented by the following tallies?

A. 11   C. 16
B. 14   D. 18

Difficulty: Easy

4. 50. Which number is represented by the following tallies?

A. 11   C. 16
B. 14   D. 15

Difficulty: Easy

5. Which number is 8 groups of 10?

A. 70   C. 90
B. 80   D. 100

Difficulty: Easy

6. Which number is 4 groups of 10?

A. 20   C. 40
B. 30   D. 50

Difficulty: Easy

7. Which number is 3 groups of 10?

A. 3   C. 20
B. 10   D. 30

Difficulty: Easy

8. Which number is 9 groups of 10?

A. 9   C. 90
B. 10   D. 100

Difficulty: Easy

9. Which number is 2 groups of 10?

A. 20   C. 40
B. 30   D. 50

Difficulty: Easy

10. Which number is 6 groups of 10?

A. 30   C. 60
B. 70   D. 50

Difficulty: Easy

11. Which number is 7 groups of 10?

A. 30   C. 60
B. 70   D. 50

Difficulty: Easy

12. Which number is 5 groups of 10?

A. 30   C. 60
B. 70   D. 50

Difficulty: Easy

13. Which number makes the comparison correct? _____ < 42

A. 49   C. 89
B. 22   D. 64

Difficulty: Easy

14. Which number makes the comparison correct? _____ > 86

A. 18   C. 81
B. 69   D. 96

Difficulty: Easy

15. Which number makes the comparison correct? _____ = 24

A. 10 + 4   C. 40 + 2
B. 20 + 4   D. 20 + 40

Difficulty: Easy

16. Which number makes the comparison correct? 82 < _____

A. 92   C. 72
B. 82   D. 62

Difficulty: Easy

1. Explanation: 17 is correct because 17 is a bundle of 10 and seven ones.

    The correct answer is D.

2. Explanation: 11 is correct because 11 is a bundle of 10 and one one.

    The correct answer is A.

3. Explanation: 18 is correct because 18 is a bundle of 10 and eight ones.

    The correct answer is D.

4. Explanation: 14 is correct because 14 is a bundle of 10 and four ones.

    The correct answer is B.

5. Explanation: 8 groups of 10 gives you an 8 in the tens place and a 0 in the ones place.

    The correct answer is B.

6. Explanation: 4 groups of 10 gives you a 4 in the tens place and a 0 in the ones place.

    The correct answer is C.

7. Explanation: 3 groups of 10 gives you a 3 in the tens place and a 0 in the ones place.

    The correct answer is D.

8. Explanation: 9 groups of 10 gives you a 9 in the tens place and a 0 in the ones place.

    The correct answer is C.

9. Explanation: 2 groups of 10 gives you a 2 in the tens place and a 0 in the ones place.

    The correct answer is A.

10. Explanation: 6 groups of 10 gives you a 6 in the tens place and a 0 in the ones place.

    The correct answer is C.

11. Explanation: 7 groups of 10 gives you a 7 in the tens place and a 0 in the ones place.

The correct answer is B.

12. Explanation: 5 groups of 10 gives you a 5 in the tens place and a 0 in the ones place.

The correct answer is D.

13. Explanation: First, you should compare the tens column. You are looking for a tens column that is equal or smaller than 4. 49 has a ten that is equal to 42, but nine is larger than 2 so that doesn't work. The correct answer has to be 22 because that is the only number that has a ten and a one smaller than 42.

The correct answer is B.

14. Explanation: First, you should compare the tens column. You are looking for a tens column that is equal or greater than 8. 81 has a ten that is equal to 86, but one is smaller than 6 so that doesn't work. The correct answer has to be 96 because that is the only number that has a ten and a one larger than 86.

The correct answer is D.

15. Explanation: The expanded form of 24 is the sum of 20 and 4.

The correct answer is B.

16. Explanation: First, you should compare the tens column. You are looking for a tens column that is equal or larger than 8. 82 has a ten that is equal to 82, but because they are equal the < sign would not be true. The correct answer has to be 92 because that is the only number that has a ten and a one larger than 82.

The correct answer is A.

1. Which number makes the comparison correct? 37 > _____

A. 67   C. 47

B. 57   D. 27

Difficulty: Easy

2. Which number makes the comparison correct? _____ < 76

A. 70 + 2   C. 70 + 8

B. 70 + 6   D. 70 + 10

Difficulty: Easy

3. Which number makes the comparison correct? 48 = _____

A. forty-eight   C. eighty-four

B. four eight   D. eight four

Difficulty: Easy

4. Which number makes the comparison correct? 92 < _____

A. 96   C. 76

B. 86   D. 66

Difficulty: Easy

5. Which number is equal to 10 bundles of 10?

A. 111   C. 100

B. 101   D. 110

Difficulty: Medium

6. Which number is equal to 70 bundles of 10?

A. 600   C. 800

B. 700   D. 900

Difficulty: Medium

7. Which number is equal to 90 bundles of 10?

A. 800   C. 600

B. 900   D. 500

Difficulty: Medium

8. Which number is equal to 60 bundles of 10?

A. 600   C. 800

B. 700   D. 900

Difficulty: Medium

9. Which number is equal to **30** bundles of 10?

A. 500   C. 300

B. 400   D. 200

Difficulty: Medium

10. Which number is equal to **20** bundles of 10?

A. 200   C. 800

B. 400   D. 700

Difficulty: Medium

11. Which number is equal to **80** bundles of 10?

A. 200   C. 800

B. 400   D. 700

Difficulty: Medium

12. Which number is equal to **40** bundles of 10?

A. 200   C. 800

B. 400   D. 700

Difficulty: Medium

13. Which number is equal to **4** hundreds?

A. 100   C. 300

B. 200   D. 400

Difficulty: Medium

14. Which number is equal to **7** hundreds?

A. 500   C. 700

B. 600   D. 800

Difficulty: Medium

15. Which number is equal to **2** hundreds?

A. 100   C. 300

B. 200   D. 400

Difficulty: Medium

16. Which number is equal to **9** hundreds?

A. 1000   C. 800

B. 900   D. 700

Difficulty: Medium

17. Which number is equal to 10 hundreds?

A. 1000   C. 800

B. 900   D. 700

Difficulty: Medium

19. Which number is equal to 3 hundreds?

A. 800   C. 600

B. 300   D. 200

Difficulty: Medium

18. Which number is equal to 6 hundreds?

A. 800   C. 600

B. 300   D. 200

Difficulty: Medium

20. Which number is equal to 8 hundreds?

A. 800   C. 600

B. 300   D. 200

Difficulty: Medium

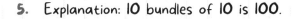

1. Explanation: First, you should compare the tens column. You are looking for a tens column that is equal or smaller than 3. The only choice that has a ten column smaller than 3 is 27.

    The correct answer is D.

2. Explanation: The expanded form of 76 is 70 + 6. The only choice smaller than 70 + 6 is 70 + 2.

    The correct answer is A.

3. Explanation: The base ten form of 48 is equal to forty plus eight or forty-eight in word form.

    The correct answer is A.

4. Explanation: To find the answer, you need to find a number larger than 92. That number must have a 9 in the tens place and a number larger than 2 in the ones place. The only choice that fits that is 96.

    The correct answer is A.

5. Explanation: 10 bundles of 10 is 100.

    The correct answer is C.

6. Explanation: 70 bundles of 10 is 700. Each ten group of bundles is another 100.

    The correct answer is B.

7. Explanation: 90 bundles of 10 is 900. Each ten group of bundles is another 100.

    The correct answer is B.

8. Explanation: 60 bundles of 10 is 600. Each ten group of bundles is another 100.

    The correct answer is A.

9. Explanation: 30 bundles of 10 is 300. Each ten group of bundles is another 100.

    The correct answer is C.

10. Explanation: 20 bundles of 10 is 200. Each ten group of bundles is another 100.

   The correct answer is A.

11. Explanation: 80 bundles of 10 is 800. Each ten group of bundles is another 100.

   The correct answer is C.

12. Explanation: 40 bundles of 10 is 400. Each ten group of bundles is another 100.

   The correct answer is B.

13. Explanation: One bundle of 100 is 100. Each additional hundred increases it by another 100. 4 bundles of hundreds is the same as 400.

   The correct answer is D.

14. Explanation: One bundle of 100 is 100. Each additional hundred increases it by another 100. 7 bundles of hundreds is the same as 700.

   The correct answer is C.

15. Explanation: One bundle of 100 is 100. Each additional hundred increases it by another 100. 2 bundles of hundreds is the same as 200.

   The correct answer is B.

16. Explanation: One bundle of 100 is 100. Each additional hundred increases it by another 100. 9 bundles of hundreds is the same as 900.

   The correct answer is B.

17. Explanation: One bundle of 100 is 100. Each additional hundred increases it by another 100. 10 bundles of hundreds is the same as 1000.

   The correct answer is A.

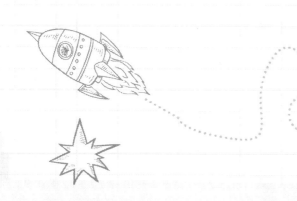

18. Explanation: One bundle of 100 is 100. Each additional hundred increases it by another 100. 6 bundles of hundreds is the same as **600**.

   The correct answer is C.

19. Explanation: One bundle of 100 is 100. Each additional hundred increases it by another 100. 3 bundles of hundreds is the same as **300**.

   The correct answer is B.

20. Explanation: One bundle of 100 is 100. Each additional hundred increases it by another 100. 8 bundles of hundreds is the same as **800**.

   The correct answer is A.

1. Which number makes the comparison correct? **632 < _____**

A. 47   C. 612
B. 329   D. 962

Difficulty: Medium

2. Which number makes the comparison correct? **983 < _____**

A. 660   C. 990
B. 770   D. 880

Difficulty: Medium

3. Which number makes the comparison correct? **_____ > 298**

A. 301   C. 269
B. 296   D. 200

Difficulty: Medium

4. Which number makes the comparison correct? **_____ > 771**

A. 750   C. 770
B. 760   D. 780

Difficulty: Medium

5. Which number makes the comparison correct? **361 = _____**

A. six hundred thirty-one
B. sixty-one
C. three hundred sixty-one
D. thirty-six

Difficulty: Medium

6. Which number makes the comparison correct? **_____ > 401**

A. 482   C. 397
B. 382   D. 391

Difficulty: Medium

7. Which number makes the comparison correct? **822 > _____**

A. 830   C. 880
B. 820   D. 900

Difficulty: Medium

BRAIN HUNTER

✱ **Numbers and Operations in Base Ten** ✱
✱ Compare by looking at 100, 10, 1s (<, >, =) ✱
✱ **Answer Explanation** ✱

1. Explanation: First you compare the hundreds column. You are looking for a number that is equal to or greater than 6. 6 and 9 both work. Next you compare the tens column and look for a number that is greater than 3. 612 is smaller than 632 because 3 is greater than 1, so that choice doesn't work. 962 is the only number that works because 9 is greater than 6.

   The correct answer is D.

2. Explanation: First you compare the hundreds column. You are looking for a number that is equal or larger than 9. The only choice that works is 990. To check, ensure that the tens column is larger. 9 is larger than 8 so 990 is larger than 983.

   The correct answer is C.

3. Explanation: First, you compare the hundreds column. Three numbers have 2s in the hundreds column so they could be right, however the only number with 2 in the hundreds column that would be larger than 298 is 299, which none of these numbers are. So the correct answer is 301 because 3 is larger than 2.

   The correct answer is A.

4. Explanation: First, we compare the hundreds column. They all are equal, so we need to compare the 10s column. The only choice that has a number larger than 7 is D, with an 8.

   The correct answer is D.

5. Explanation: To write 361 in words, you need to express that there are three hundreds. The only answer that does that is C.

   The correct answer is C.

6. Explanation: First, we compare the hundreds column. To be larger than 401, the hundreds must be four or above. Next, we look at the ones column. The only number that is larger than 401 is 482 because 8 is larger than 0.

   The correct answer is A.

7. Explanation: First, we compare the hundreds. To be larger than 822, the hundreds must be eight or smaller. Next we compare the tens column. We need a number that is equal or smaller than 2. The only choice that makes sense is B.

   The correct answer is B.

1. 34 + 7 =

A. 41   C. 43
B. 42   D. 44

Difficulty: Easy

2. 28 + 5 =

A. 30   C. 32
B. 31   D. 33

Difficulty: Easy

3. 76 - 2 =

A. 75   C. 73
B. 74   D. 72

Difficulty: Easy

4. 81 - 4 =

A. 77   C. 75
B. 76   D. 74

Difficulty: Easy

5. 47 + 6 =

A. 51   C. 53
B. 52   D. 54

Difficulty: Easy

6. 68 - 3 =

A. 69   C. 66
B. 67   D. 65

Difficulty: Easy

7. 93 + 8 =

A. 101   C. 102
B. 100   D. 103

Difficulty: Easy

8. 56 + 5 =

A. 60   C. 62
B. 61   D. 63

Difficulty: Easy

9. 22 - 9 =

A. 13   C. 11
B. 12   D. 10

Difficulty: Easy

10. What is 10 more than 80?

A. 90   C. 70
B. 80   D. 60

Difficulty: Easy

11. What is 10 less than 70?

A. 40   C. 60
B. 50   D. 70

Difficulty: Easy

12. What is 10 more than 40?

A. 20   C. 40
B. 30   D. 50

Difficulty: Easy

13. What is 10 less than 20?

A. 0   C. 20
B. 10   D. 30

Difficulty: Easy

14. What is ten more than 90?

A. 40   C. 80
B. 60   D. 100

Difficulty: Easy

15. What is ten more than 10?

A. 10   C. 30
B. 20   D. 40

Difficulty: Easy

16. What is ten less than 30?

A. 80   C. 20
B. 60   D. 40

Difficulty: Easy

17. What is ten more than 60?

A. 30   C. 70
B. 50   D. 90

Difficulty: Easy

18. What is ten less than 50?

A. 40   C. 80
B. 60   D. 100

Difficulty: Easy

19. 40 - 20 =

A. 20   C. 40
B. 30   D. 50

Difficulty: Easy

20. 80 - 60 =

A. 20   C. 40
B. 30   D. 50

Difficulty: Easy

※ Numbers and Operations in Base Ten ※
※ Using place value to perform operations ※
※ Answer Explanation ※

1. Explanation: To solve this problem, you should count on 7 from 34: 34, 35, 36, 37, 38, 39, 40, 41.

   The correct answer is A.

2. Explanation: To solve this problem, you should count on 5 from 28: 28, 29, 30, 31, 32.

   The correct answer is D.

3. Explanation: To solve this problem, you should count down 2 from 76: 76, 75, 74.

   The correct answer is B.

4. Explanation: To solve this problem, you should count down 4 from 81: 81, 80, 79, 78, 77.

   The correct answer is A.

5. Explanation: To solve this problem, you should count up 6 from 47: 47, 48, 49, 50, 51, 52, 53.

   The correct answer is C.

6. Explanation: To solve this problem, you should count down 3 from 68: 68, 67, 66, 65.

   The correct answer is D.

7. Explanation: To solve this problem, you should count up 8 from 93: 93, 94, 95, 96, 97, 98, 99, 100, 101.

   The correct answer is A.

8. Explanation: To solve this problem, you should count up 5 from 56: 56, 57, 58, 59, 60, 61.

   The correct answer is B.

9. Explanation: To solve this problem, you should count down 9 from 22: 22, 21, 20, 19, 18, 17, 16, 15, 14, 13.

   The correct answer is A.

10. Explanation: To solve this problem, count up by 10s from 80: 80, 90.

    The correct answer is A.

✳ **Numbers and Operations in Base Ten** ✳
✳ Using place value to perform operations ✳
✳ **Answer Explanation** ✳

11. Explanation: To solve this problem, count down by 10s from 70: 70, 60.

The correct answer is C.

12. Explanation: To solve this problem, count up by 10s from 40: 40, 50.

The correct answer is D.

13. Explanation: To solve this problem, count down by 10 from 20: 20, 10.

The correct answer is B.

14. Explanation: To solve this problem, count up by 10 from 90: 90, 100.

The correct answer is D.

15. Explanation: To solve this problem, count up by 10 from 10: 10, 20.

The correct answer is B.

16. Explanation: To solve this problem, count down by 10 from 30: 30, 20.

The correct answer is C.

17. Explanation: To solve this problem, count up by 10 from 60: 60, 70.

The correct answer is C.

18. Explanation: To solve this problem, count down by 10 from 50: 50, 40.

The correct answer is A.

19. Explanation: 40 - 20 is the same as 4 - 2, just adding the multiple of 10. So 2 becomes 20.

The correct answer is A.

20. Explanation: 80 - 60 is the same as 8 - 6, just adding the multiple of 10. So 2 becomes 20.

The correct answer is A.

1. 50 - 20 =

A. 50 C. 30
B. 40 D. 20

Difficulty: Easy

2. 90 - 30 =

A. 90 C. 70
B. 80 D. 60

Difficulty: Easy

3. 30 - 10 =

A. 10 C. 30
B. 20 D. 40

Difficulty: Easy

4. 50 - 30 =

A. 10 C. 30
B. 20 D. 40

Difficulty: Easy

5. 60 - 50 =

A. 10 C. 30
B. 20 D. 40

Difficulty: Easy

6. 70 - 20 =

A. 30 C. 50
B. 40 D. 60

Difficulty: Easy

7. 90 - 40 =

A. 80 C. 60
B. 70 D. 50

Difficulty: Easy

8. 20 - 10 =

A. 0 C. 20
B. 10 D. 30

Difficulty: Easy

9. 63 + 27 =

A. 90 C. 70
B. 80 D. 60

Difficulty: Medium

10. 41 - 38 =

A. 6 C. 4
B. 5 D. 3

Difficulty: Medium

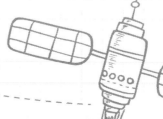

11. 83 + 7 =

A. 70   C. 90
B. 80   D. 100

16. 78 - 51 =

A. 27   C. 28
B. 36   D. 18

12. 64 - 19 =

A. 35   C. 55
B. 45   D. 65

17. 35 + 8 =

A. 42   C. 44
B. 43   D. 45

13. 26 + 14 =

A. 40   C. 50
B. 30   D. 20

18. 22 + 45 + 37 =

A. 104   C. 82
B. 67   D. 149

14. 97 - 32 =

A. 54   C. 55
B. 64   D. 65

19. 42 + 91 + 13 =

A. 146   C. 104
B. 133   D. 237

15. 65 - 27 =

A. 18   C. 38
B. 28   D. 48

BRAIN HUNTER

✳ **Numbers and Operations in Base Ten** ✳
✳ Using place value to perform operations ✳
✳ Answer Explanation ✳

1. Explanation: 50 - 20 is the same as 5 - 2, just adding the multiple of 10. So 3 becomes 30.

   The correct answer is C.

2. Explanation: 90 - 30 is the same as 9 - 3, just adding the multiple of 10. So 6 becomes 60.

   The correct answer is D.

3. Explanation: 30 - 10 is the same as 3 - 1, just adding the multiple of 10. So 2 becomes 20.

   The correct answer is B.

4. Explanation: 50 - 30 is the same as 5 - 3, just adding the multiple of 10. So 2 becomes 20.

   The correct answer is B.

5. Explanation: 60 - 50 is the same as 6 - 5, just adding the multiple of 10. So 1 becomes 10.

   The correct answer is A.

6. Explanation: 70 - 20 is the same as 7 - 2, just adding the multiple of 10. So 5 becomes 50.

   The correct answer is C.

7. Explanation: 90 - 40 is the same as 9 - 4, just adding the multiple of 10. So 5 becomes 50.

   The correct answer is D.

8. Explanation: 20 - 10 is the same as 2 - 1, just adding the multiple of 10. So 1 becomes 10.

   The correct answer is B.

9. Explanation: First, you add the ones column, which gives you 10. You place the 0 and carry the 1. Then you add 6 + 2 + 1, which equals 9. So the correct answer is 90.

   The correct answer is A.

10. Explanation: First you try to subtract 8 from 1. You have to borrow from the 4 to make it 11. 11 - 8 is 3. Then you subtract 3 - 3, which gives you 0. So, the correct answer is 3.

    The correct answer is D.

11. Explanation: To solve this problem, you can count seven on 83: 83, 84, 85, 86, 87, 88, 89, 90.

    The correct answer is C.

✴ **Numbers and Operations in Base Ten** ✴
✴ Using place value to perform operations ✴
✴ **Answer Explanation** ✴

BRAIN HUNTER

12. Explanation: To solve this problem, you should first try to subtract 9 from 4. You can't do that so you borrow one from the 6. The six becomes a 5 and you take 14 - 9, which gives you 5. Then you take, 5 - 1, which gives you 4 making the answer 45.

The correct answer is B.

13. Explanation: To solve this problem, first you add 4 + 6, which equals the 10. You write down the 0 and carry the one. the next step is to add 2 + 1 + 1, which equals 4, making the answer 40.

The correct answer is A.

14. Explanation: To solve this problem, first you subtract 7 - 2, which equals 5. Then you subtract 9 - 3, which equals 6, making the answer 65.

The correct answer is D.

15. Explanation: To solve this problem, first you need to borrow 1 from the 6, making it 5 and making the 5 15. Next, you take 15 - 7, which is 8. Then you take 5 - 2, which is 3, making the answer 38.

The correct answer is C.

16. Explanation: First you take 8 - 7, which gives you 7. Next, you take 7 - 5, which gives you 2, making the answer 27.

The correct answer is A.

17. Explanation: To solve this problem, count up 8 from 35: 35, 36, 37, 38, 39, 40, 41, 42, 43.

The correct answer is B.

18. Explanation: To find the correct answer, first you add 22 + 45. When you add 2 + 5, you get 7 and when you add 2 + 4, you get 6 for an answer of 67. Next you add 67 + 37. 7 + 7 = 14. Put down the 4, carry the 1. 6 + 3 + 1 is 10, making the answer 104.

The correct answer is A.

19. Explanation: First, you add 42 + 91. 1 + 2 = 3 and then 4 + 9 = 13, making the answer 133. Next you add 133 + 13. 3 + 3 is 6, next 3 + 1 is 4 and then 1 + 0 = 1. So your final answer is 146.

The correct answer is A.

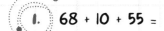
1. 68 + 10 + 55 =

A. 65   C. 123
B. 78   D. 133

Difficulty: Medium

2. 71 + 86 + 23 + 14 =

A. 157   C. 37
B. 194   D. 85

Difficulty: Medium

3. 55 + 71 + 17 =

A. 156   C. 132
B. 113   D. 143

Difficulty: Medium

4. 82 + 47 + 32 =

A. 141   C. 161
B. 151   D. 171

Difficulty: Medium

5. 19 + 92 + 55 =

A. 155   C. 177
B. 166   D. 188

Difficulty: Medium

6. 26 + 63 + 78 =

A. 167   C. 178
B. 156   D. 189

Difficulty: Medium

7. 34 + 89 + 41 =

A. 164   C. 176
B. 153   D. 165

Difficulty: Medium

8. 863 - 428 =

A. 433   C. 453
B. 435   D. 442

Difficulty: Medium

9. 328 + 652 =

    A. 960   **C.** 980

    B. 970   **D.** 880

Difficulty: Medium

10. 921 - 743 =

    A. 154   **C.** 168

    B. 166   **D.** 178

Difficulty: Medium

11. 227 + 521 =

    A. 748   **C.** 638

    B. 648   **D.** 347

Difficulty: Medium

12. 528 + 865 =

    A. 1396   **C.** 1286

    B. 1393   **D.** 1381

Difficulty: Medium

13. 964 - 392 =

    A. 582   **C.** 572

    B. 682   **D.** 661

Difficulty: Medium

14. 430 + 710 =

    A. 1030   **C.** 1130

    B. 1040   **D.** 1140

Difficulty: Medium

15. 197 - 142 =

    A. 55   **C.** 62

    B. 61   **D.** 51

Difficulty: Medium

16. 291 + 616 =

    A. 808   **C.** 906

    B. 907   **D.** 709

Difficulty: Medium

✷ **Numbers and Operations in Base Ten** ✷
✷ Using place value to perform operations ✷
✷ **Answer Explanation** ✷

1. Explanation: First you add 10 to 68, which gives you 78. Then you add 78 + 55. 8 + 5 is 13, you carry the one so your next problem is 5 + 7 + 1, which equals 13. The correct answer is 133.

   The correct answer is D.

2. Explanation: First you add 71 + 86. 6 + 1 = 7 and 7 + 8 = 15 So that answer is 157. Next you add 23 + 14. 4 + 3 = 7 and then 2 + 1 = 3. So that answer is 37. Then finally you add 157 + 37. 7 + 7 = 14. Write down the 4 and carry the 1. 1 + 5 + 3 = 9, 1 + 0 = 0. Your final answer is 194.

   The correct answer is B.

3. Explanation: First, you add 5 + 1 + 7, which is 13. Write down the 3 and carry the 1. Next you add 1 + 5 + 7 + 1, which is 14, making the answer 143.

   The correct answer is D.

4. Explanation: First, you add 2 + 7 + 2, which is 11. Write down the 1 and carry the 1. Next, you add 1 + 8 + 4 + 3, which is 16, making the answer 161.

   The correct answer is C.

5. Explanation: First, you add 9 + 2 + 5, which is 16. Write down the 6 and carry the 1. Next, you add 1 + 1 + 9 + 5, which is 16, making the answer 166.

   The correct answer is B.

6. Explanation: First, you add 6 + 3 + 8, which is 17. Write down the 7 and carry the 1. Next, you add 1 + 2 + 6 + 7, which is 16, making the answer 167.

   The correct answer is A.

7. Explanation: First, you add 4 + 1 + 9, which is 14. Write down the 4 and carry the 1. Next, you add 1 + 3 + 8 + 4, which is 16, making the answer 164.

   The correct answer is A.

8. Explanation: First, you try to subtract 3 - 8. You cannot so you have to borrow one from the 6. Then, you subtract 13 - 8 = 5. Next you subtract 5 - 2, which equals 3. Finally, you subtract 8 - 4, which equals 4, for an answer of 435.

   The correct answer is B.

9. Explanation: First, you add 8 + 2 = 10. You write down the 0 and carry the 1. Next you add 1 + 2 + 5, which equals

✳ **Numbers and Operations in Base Ten** ✳
✳ Using place value to perform operations ✳
✳ **Answer Explanation** ✳

8. Finally, you add **6 + 3**, which equals **9** for a final answer of **980**.

The correct answer is C.

10. Explanation: First you try to subtract **3** from **1**. You cannot, so you borrow **1** from the **2**, making it **11 - 3**, which is **8**. Next, you try to subtract **4** from **1**, which you cannot, so you borrow from the **9**, making that problem **11 - 4**, which is **7**. Finally, you subtract **8 - 7** = **1**. Your final answer is **178**.

The correct answer is D.

11. Explanation: First, you add **7 + 1 = 8**. Next, you add **2 + 2**, which equals **4**. Finally, you add **2 + 5**, which equals **7**. Finally, when you put your solution together, you get **748**.

The correct answer is A.

12. Explanation: First, you add **8 + 5**. That gives you **13**, so you write down the **3** and carry the **1**. Next you add **1 + 2 + 6**, which gives you **9**. Finally, you add **5 + 8**, which gives you **13** for the answer of **1393**.

The correct answer is B.

13. Explanation: First, you take **4 - 2**, which equals **2**. Next you need to borrow **1** from the **9** in **964**, so you can make **6, 16**. Then, you take **16 - 9**, which is **7**. Finally, you take **8 - 5**, which is **5**, making the correct answer **572**.

The correct answer is C.

14. Explanation: First you add **1 + 3**, which is **4**. Then, you add **4 + 7**, which is **11**, making the final answer **1140**.

The correct answer is D.

15. Explanation: First, you take **7 - 2**, which is **5**. Next you take **9 - 4**, which is **5**. Finally, you take **1 - 1**, which is **0**, making the final answer **55**.

The correct answer is A.

16. Explanation: First, you take **1 + 6**, which equals **7**. Next, you add **9 + 1**, which is **10**, so you write down the **0** and carry the **1**. Finally, you take **1 + 2 + 6**, which is **9**, making the final answer **907**.

The correct answer is B.

1. 650 - 10 =

A. 550   C. 660

B. 750   D. 640

Difficulty: Medium

2. 480 + 10 =

A. 491   C. 490

B. 500   D. 49

Difficulty: Medium

3. 730 + 100 =

A. 830   C. 731

B. 740   D. 173

Difficulty: Medium

4. 590 - 100 =

A. 490   C. 480

B. 49   D. 48

Difficulty: Medium

5. 290 + 10 =

A. 270   C. 210

B. 280   D. 300

Difficulty: Medium.

6. 350 - 10 =

A. 360   C. 340

B. 350   D. 330

Difficulty: Medium

7. 640 + 100 =

A. 540   C. 740

B. 640   D. 840

Difficulty: Medium

8. 920 - 100 =

A. 820   C. 1020

B. 720   D. 1120

Difficulty: Medium

9. 870 - 100 =

A. 670   C. 870

B. 770   D. 970

Difficulty: Medium

10. What number makes the following problem true? _____ + 328 = 790

A. 362   C. 461

B. 462   D. 360

Difficulty: Medium

11. What number makes the following problem true? _____ - 279 = 573

A. 861 C. 852

B. 742 D. 952

Difficulty: Medium

12. What number makes the following problem true? 24 + _____ = 115

A. 72 C. 81

B. 82 D. 91

Difficulty: Medium

13. What number makes the following problem true? 76 - _____ = 25

A. 51 C. 71

B. 61 D. 81

Difficulty: Medium

14. What number makes the following problem true? _____ + 23 = 79

A. 66 C. 75

B. 56 D. 57

Difficulty: Medium

15. What number makes the following problem true? _____ - 829 = 116

A. 944 C. 945

B. 955 D. 935

Difficulty: Medium

16. What number makes the following problem true? 42 - _____ =16

A. 26 C. 46

B. 36 D. 56

Difficulty: Medium

17. What number makes the following problem true? 67 + _____ = 127

A. 40 C. 70

B. 50 D. 60

Difficulty: Medium

BRAIN HUNTER

✳ **Numbers and Operations in Base Ten** ✳
✳ Using place value to perform operations ✳
✳ **Answer Explanation** ✳

1. Explanation: This is the same as subtracting 65 - 1, which is 64. Then, you add the 10 back on for a final answer of 640.

   The correct answer is D.

2. Explanation: This is the same as adding 48 + 1, which is 49. Then, you add the 10 back on for a final answer of 490.

   The correct answer is C.

3. Explanation: This is the same as adding 73 + 10, which is 83. Then, you add the 10 back on for a final answer of 830.

   The correct answer is A.

4. Explanation: This is the same as subtracting 59 - 10, which is 49. Then, you add the 10 back on for a final answer of 490.

   The correct answer is A.

5. Explanation: This is the same as adding 29 + 1, which is 30. Then, you add the 10 back on for a final answer of 300.

   The correct answer is D.

6. Explanation: This is the same as subtracting 35 - 1, which is 34. Then, you add the 10 back on for a final answer of 340.

   The correct answer is C.

7. Explanation: This is the same as adding 64 + 10, which is 74. Then, you add the 10 back on for a final answer of 740.

   The correct answer is C.

8. Explanation: This is the same as subtracting 92 - 10, which is 82. Then, you add the 10 back on for a final answer of 820.

   The correct answer is A.

9. Explanation: This is the same as subtracting 87 - 10, which is 77. Then, you add the 10 back on for a final answer of 770.

   The correct answer is B.

BRAIN HUNTER

✳ **Numbers and Operations in Base Ten** ✳
✳ Using place value to perform operations ✳
✳ Answer Explanation ✳

10. Explanation: To solve this problem, you actually need to take 790 - 328. You have to borrow from the 9 to make it 10 - 8 = 2. Next you take 8 - 2, which is 6 and then you take 7 - 3, which is 4. The final answer is 462.

The correct answer is B.

11. Explanation: To solve, first you add 279 and 573. 3 + 9 = 12, write down the 2 and carry the 1. Next you add 1 + 7 + 7, which is 15. Write down the 5 and carry the 1. Finally, you add 1 + 2 + 5, which is 8. Your final answer is 852.

The correct answer is C.

12. Explanation: To solve, you have to take 115 - 24. 5 - 4 = 1, next you take 1 - 2, which you cannot do so you borrow from the 100s 1. 11 - 2 = 9. Your final answer is 91.

The correct answer is D.

13. Explanation: To solve, you take 76 - 25. First, 6 - 5 = 1. Next you take 7 - 2, which is 5. The final answer is 51.

The correct answer is A.

14. Explanation: To solve, you take 79 - 23. First, you take 9 - 3, which is 6 and then you take 7 - 2, which is 5, making the answer 56.

The correct answer is B.

15. Explanation: First you add 829 and 116. You take 6+9, which is 15, write down the 5 and carry the 1. Next, you take 1 + 2 + 1, which is 4. Finally, you take 8 + 1, which is 9, making the answer 945.

The correct answer is C.

16. Explanation: You need to subtract 42 - 16. First, you cannot subtract 6 from 2, so you need to borrow one from the 4. Then, you take 12 - 6, which is 6, followed by 3 - 1, which is 2, giving you an answer of 26.

The correct answer is A.

17. Explanation: To find the answer, you take 127 - 67. First, you take 7 - 7, which is 0. Next, you take 12 - 6, which gives you an answer of 6, making the problem's answer 60.

The correct answer is D.

1. What number makes the following problem true? _____ + 128 = 183

A. 44   C. 66

B. 55   D. 77

Difficulty: Medium

2. What number makes the following problem true? 678 - _____ = 444

A. 234   C. 324

B. 243   D. 432

Difficulty: Medium

3. 50 × 8 =

A. 200   C. 40

B. 58   D. 400

Difficulty: Hard

4. 30 × 7 =

A. 370   C. 21

B. 200   D. 210

Difficulty: Hard

5. 20 × 9 =

A. 1800   C. 180

B. 29   D. 18

Difficulty: Hard

6. 60 × 5 =

A. 30   C. 305

B. 300   D. 3300

Difficulty: Hard

7. 90 × 3 =

A. 27   C. 2710

B. 270   D. 2700

Difficulty: Hard

8. 80 × 2 =

A. 160   C. 32

B. 16   D. 320

Difficulty: Hard

9. 40 × 6 =

A. 32   C. 24

B. 320   D. 240

Difficulty: Hard

10. 70 × 4 =

A. 140   C. 280
B. 14   D. 28

Difficulty: Hard

11. 10 × 8 =

A. 80   C. 70
B. 90   D. 60

Difficulty: Hard

12. 60 × 9 =

A. 450   C. 630
B. 540   D. 720

Difficulty: Hard

13. 20 × 6 =

A. 60   C. 100
B. 80   D. 120

Difficulty: Hard

14. 80 × 4 =

A. 240   C. 320
B. 280   D. 300

Difficulty: Hard

15. 30 × 7 =

A. 190   C. 210
B. 200   D. 220

Difficulty: Hard

16. 90 × 5 =

A. 440   C. 460
B. 450   D. 470

Difficulty: Hard

17. 50 × 8 =

A. 400   C. 500
B. 450   D. 550

Difficulty: Hard

BRAIN HUNTER

✸ **Numbers and Operations in Base Ten** ✸
✸ Using place value to perform operations ✸
✸ **Answer Explanation** ✸

1. Explanation: To solve, you take 183 - 128. First, you borrow 1 from the 8 in 183, to make the first problem 13 - 8. That gives you an answer of 5. Next, you take 7 - 2, for an answer of 5. Finally, you take 1 - 1, which is 0, giving you an answer of 55.

   The correct answer is B.

2. Explanation: First, you take 678 - 444. 8 - 4 is 4. Next, you take 7 - 4, which is 3. Finally, you take 6 - 4, which is 2, making your final answer 234.

   The correct answer is A.

3. Explanation: To solve, you take 5 x 8, which is 40 and then you add a 0 for the 50.

   The correct answer is D.

4. Explanation: To solve, you take 3 x 7, which is 21 and then you add a 0 for the 30.

   The correct answer is D.

5. Explanation: To solve, you take 2 x 9, which is 18 and then you add a 0 for the 20.

   The correct answer is C.

6. Explanation: To solve, you take 6 x 5, which is 30 and then you add a 0 for the 60.

   The correct answer is B.

7. Explanation: First, you take 9 x 3, which is 27 and then you add a 0 for the 90.

   The correct answer is B.

8. Explanation: First you take 8 x 2, which is 16 and then you add a 0 for the 80.

   The correct answer is A.

9. Explanation: First you take 4 x 6, which is 24 and then you add a 0 for the 40.

   The correct answer is D.

BRAIN HUNTER

✳ **Numbers and Operations in Base Ten** ✳
✳ Using place value to perform operations ✳
✳ **Answer Explanation** ✳

10. Explanation: First, you take 7 x 4, which is 28 and then you add a 0 for the 70.

   The correct answer is C.

11. Explanation: First, you take 1 x 8, which is 8 and then you add a 0 for the 80.

   The correct answer is A.

12. Explanation: First, you take 6 x 9, which is 54 and then you add a 0 for the 60.

   The correct answer is B.

13. Explanation: First, you take 2 x 6, which is 12 and then you add a 0 for the 20.

   The correct answer is D.

14. Explanation: First, you take 8 x 4, which is 32 and then you add a 0 for the 80.

   The correct answer is C.

15. Explanation: First, you take 3 x 7, which is 21 and then you add a 0 for the 30.

   The correct answer is C.

16. Explanation: First, you take 9 x 5, which is 45 and then you add a 0 for the 90.

   The correct answer is B.

17. Explanation: First, you take 5 x 8, which is 40 and then you add a 0 for the 50.

   The correct answer is A.

Numbers, Operations, and Fractions

1. Dividing Shapes into Equal Parts page 112

2. Understanding Fractions page 134

3. Comparing Fractions page 155

1. Which circle is divided into 2 equal shares?

A.

B.

C.

D.

Difficulty: Easy

2. Which circle is divided into 4 equal shares?

A.

B.

C.

D.

Difficulty: Easy

3. Which circle is divided into 2 equal shares?

A.

B.

C.

D.

Difficulty: Easy

4. Which circle is divided into 4 equal shares?

A.

B.

C.

D.

Difficulty: Easy

5. Which rectangle is divided into 2 equal shares?

A.

B.

C.

D.

Difficulty: Easy

6. Which rectangle is divided into 4 equal shares?

A.

B.

C.

D.

Difficulty: Easy

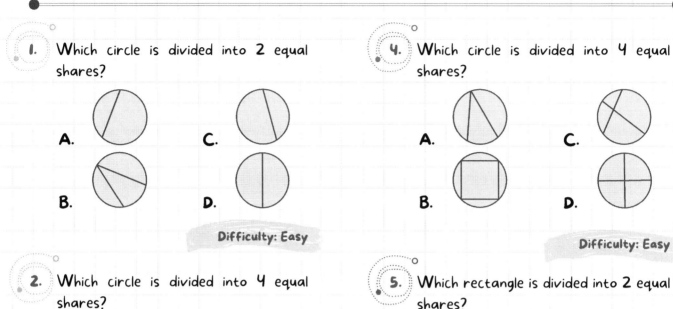
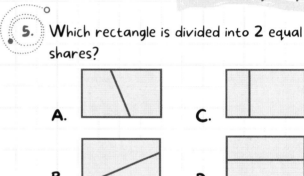
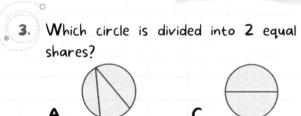
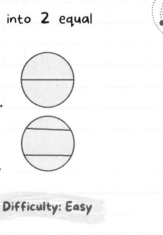
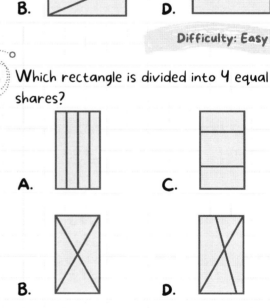

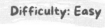

7. Which rectangle is divided into 2 equal shares?

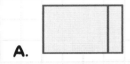

A.

C.

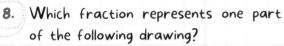

B.

D.

Difficulty: Easy

8. Which fraction represents one part of the following drawing?

A. $\dfrac{2}{1}$

C. $\dfrac{1}{1}$

B. $\dfrac{1}{2}$

D. $\dfrac{2}{2}$

Difficulty: Easy

9. Which fraction represents one part of the following drawing?

A. $\dfrac{1}{2}$

C. $\dfrac{1}{1}$

B. $\dfrac{2}{2}$

D. $\dfrac{2}{1}$

Difficulty: Easy

10. How many equal shares is the following circle divided into?

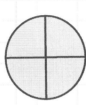

A. 1   C. 5

B. 4   D. 3

Difficulty: Easy

11. How many equal shares is the following rectangle divided into?

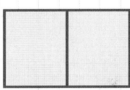

A. 2   C. 4

B. 3   D. 5

Difficulty: Easy

12. Divide the rectangle into 4 equal shares.

Difficulty: Easy

1. Explanation: This shape is the only one that contains a line that divides it into two smaller shapes of the same size.

   The correct answer is D.

2. Explanation: This shape is the only one that contains two lines that divide it into four smaller shapes of the same size.

   The correct answer is B.

3. Explanation: This shape is the only one that contains a line that divides it into two smaller shapes of the same size.

   The correct answer is C.

4. Explanation: This shape is the only one that contains two lines that divide it into four smaller shapes of the same size.

   The correct answer is D.

5. Explanation: This shape is the only one that contains a line that divides it into two smaller shapes of the same size.

   The correct answer is D.

6. Explanation: This shape is the only one that contains lines that divide it into four smaller shapes of the same size.

   The correct answer is A.

7. Explanation: This shape is the only one that contains a line that divides it into two smaller shapes of the same size.

   The correct answer is C.

8. Explanation: This shape is divided into 2 equal parts. One part is represented by the 1 on top of the fraction and the two parts are represented by the two on the bottom of the fraction.

   The correct answer is B.

9. Explanation: This shape is divided into 2 equal parts. One part is represented by the 1 on top of the fraction and the two parts are represented by the two on the bottom of the fraction.

   The correct answer is A.

10. Explanation: The lines divide the shape into four smaller but same size shapes.

    The correct answer is B.

11. Explanation: The line divides the shape into two smaller but same size shapes

    The correct answer is A.

12. Explanation: To divide a shape into equal shares, you need to draw a line within the shape that divides it, but make sure each smaller shape is equal.

    Students should draw two lines in the shape, dividing it into four smaller but equal shapes.

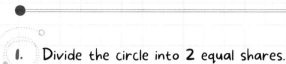

1. Divide the circle into **2** equal shares.

Difficulty: Easy

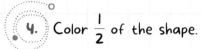**4.** Color $\frac{1}{2}$ of the shape.

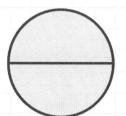

Difficulty: Easy

2. Color $\frac{1}{2}$ of the shape.

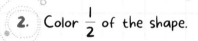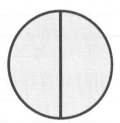

Difficulty: Easy

5. Color $\frac{1}{2}$ of the shape.

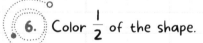

Difficulty: Easy

3. Color $\frac{1}{2}$ of the shape.

Difficulty: Easy

6. Color $\frac{1}{2}$ of the shape.

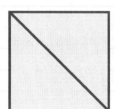

Difficulty: Easy

7. Which rectangle is divided into equal shares?

A.

C.

B.

D.

Difficulty: Medium

8. Which rectangle is divided into equal shares?

A.

C.

B.

D.

Difficulty: Medium

9. Which rectangle is divided into equal shares?

A.

C.

B.

D.

Difficulty: Medium

10. Which rectangle is divided into equal shares?

A.

C.

B.

D.

Difficulty: Medium

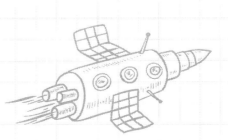

1. Explanation: To divide a shape into equal shares, you need to draw a line within the shape that divides it but make sure each smaller shape is equal.
Students should draw one line in the shape, dividing it into two smaller but equal shapes.

2. Explanation: When a shape is divided into 2, if you color 1 part, you will have colored $\frac{1}{2}$.
Student should only color $\frac{1}{2}$ of the shape.

3. Explanation: When a shape is divided into 2, if you color 1 part, you will have colored $\frac{1}{2}$.
Student should only color $\frac{1}{2}$ of the shape.

4. Explanation: When a shape is divided into 2, if you color 1 part, you will have colored $\frac{1}{2}$.
Student should only color $\frac{1}{2}$ of the shape.

5. Explanation: When a shape is divided into 2, if you color 1 part, you will have colored $\frac{1}{2}$.
Student should only color $\frac{1}{2}$ of the shape.

6. Explanation: When a shape is divided into 2, if you color 1 part, you will have colored $\frac{1}{2}$.
Student should only color $\frac{1}{2}$ of the shape.

7. Explanation: This shape is the only one that contains lines that divide it into six smaller shapes of the same size.
The correct answer is A.

8. Explanation: This shape is the only one that contains lines that divide it into six smaller shapes of the same size.
The correct answer is C.

9. Explanation: This shape is the only one that contains lines that divide it into six smaller shapes of the same size.
The correct answer is A.

10. Explanation: This shape is the only one that contains lines that divide it into twelve smaller shapes of the same size.
The correct answer is A.

1. How many equal shares is the following rectangle divided into?

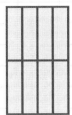

A. 2   C. 6
B. 4   D. 8

Difficulty: Medium

2. How many equal shares is the following rectangle divided into?

A. 3   C. 9
B. 6   D. 12

Difficulty: : Medium

3. How many equal shares is the following rectangle divided into?

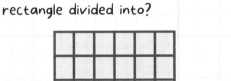

A. 18   C. 12
B. 9   D. 6

Difficulty: Medium

4. How many equal shares is the following rectangle divided into?

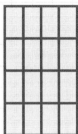

A. 8   C. 12
B. 16   D. 6

Difficulty: Medium

5. How many equal shares is the following rectangle divided into?

A. 4   C. 6
B. 3   D. 12

Difficulty: Medium

6. Which fraction represents one part of the following rectangle?

A. $\frac{1}{1}$ C. $\frac{1}{3}$

B. $\frac{1}{2}$ D. $\frac{1}{4}$

Difficulty: Medium

8. Which fraction represents one part of the following rectangle?

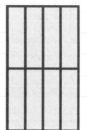

A. $\frac{1}{2}$ C. $\frac{1}{6}$

B. $\frac{1}{4}$ D. $\frac{1}{8}$

Difficulty: Medium

7. Which fraction represents one part of the following rectangle?

A. $\frac{1}{3}$ C. $\frac{1}{5}$

B. $\frac{1}{4}$ D. $\frac{1}{6}$

Difficulty: Medium

9. Which fraction represents one part of the following rectangle?

A. $\frac{1}{9}$ C. $\frac{1}{3}$

B. $\frac{1}{6}$ D. $\frac{1}{2}$

Difficulty: Medium

10. Which fraction represents one part of the following rectangle?

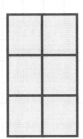

A. $\dfrac{1}{6}$

C. $\dfrac{1}{2}$

B. $\dfrac{1}{12}$

D. $\dfrac{1}{4}$

Difficulty: Medium

11. Divide the rectangle into 12 equal shares.

Difficulty: Medium

12. Divide the rectangle into 10 equal shares.

Difficulty: Medium

13. Divide the rectangle into 6 equal shares.

Difficulty: Medium

14. If a shape is divided into 2 equal parts, which fraction would represent one part?

A. $\dfrac{1}{4}$

C. $\dfrac{1}{6}$

B. $\dfrac{1}{2}$

D. $\dfrac{1}{3}$

Difficulty: Medium

15. If a shape is divided into 3 equal parts, which fraction would represent one part?

A. $\dfrac{1}{3}$

C. $\dfrac{1}{5}$

B. $\dfrac{1}{4}$

D. $\dfrac{1}{6}$

Difficulty: Medium

1. Explanation: This shape contains lines that divide it into eight smaller but equal shapes.

   The correct answer is D.

2. Explanation: This shape contains lines that divide it into nine smaller but equal shapes.

   The correct answer is C.

3. Explanation: This shape contains lines that divide it into eighteen smaller but equal shapes.

   The correct answer is A.

4. Explanation: This shape contains lines that divide it into sixteen smaller but equal shapes.

   The correct answer is B.

5. Explanation: This shape contains lines that divide it into six smaller but equal shapes.

   The correct answer is C.

6. Explanation: This shape is divided into 3 equal parts. One part is represented by the 1 on top of the fraction and the three parts are represented by the three on the bottom of the fraction.

   The correct answer is C.

7. Explanation: This shape is divided into 6 equal parts. One part is represented by the 1 on top of the fraction and the six parts are represented by the six on the bottom of the fraction.

   The correct answer is D.

8. Explanation: This shape is divided into 8 equal parts. One part is represented by the 1 on top of the fraction and the eight parts are represented by the eight on the bottom of the fraction.

   The correct answer is D.

9. Explanation: This shape is divided into 9 equal parts. One part is represented by the 1 on top of the fraction and the nine parts are represented by the nine on the bottom of the fraction.

   The correct answer is A.

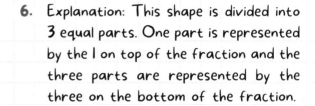

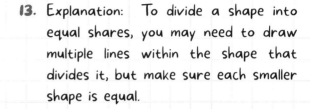
10. Explanation: This shape is divided into **6** equal parts. One part is represented by the **1** on top of the fraction and the six parts are represented by the six on the bottom of the fraction.

The correct answer is A.

11. Explanation: To divide a shape into equal shares, you may need to draw multiple lines within the shape that divides it, but make sure each smaller shape is equal.

Students should draw lines in the shape, dividing it into twelve smaller but equal shapes.

12. Explanation: To divide a shape into equal shares, you may need to draw multiple lines within the shape that divides it, but make sure each smaller shape is equal.

Students should draw lines in the shape, dividing it into ten smaller but equal shapes.

13. Explanation: To divide a shape into equal shares, you may need to draw multiple lines within the shape that divides it, but make sure each smaller shape is equal.

Students should draw lines in the shape, dividing it into six smaller but equal shapes.

14. Explanation: If a shape is divided into **2** equal parts, each individual part would represent $\frac{1}{2}$ of the whole shape.

The correct answer is B.

15. Explanation: If a shape is divided into **3** equal parts, each individual part would represent $\frac{1}{3}$ of the whole shape.

The correct answer is A.

 1. If a shape is divided into **4** equal parts, which fraction would represent one part?

A. $\frac{1}{2}$ C. $\frac{1}{4}$

B. $\frac{1}{3}$ D. $\frac{1}{5}$

Difficulty: Medium

2. If a shape is divided into **6** equal parts, which fraction would represent one part?

A. $\frac{1}{3}$ C. $\frac{1}{5}$

B. $\frac{1}{4}$ D. $\frac{1}{6}$

Difficulty: Medium

3. If a shape is divided into **8** equal parts, which fraction would represent one part?

A. $\frac{1}{6}$ C. $\frac{1}{8}$

B. $\frac{1}{3}$ D. $\frac{1}{2}$

Difficulty: Medium

4. Which circle is divided into two equal shares?

A.   C.

B.   D.

Difficulty: Medium

5. Which circle is divided into two equal shares?

A.   C.

B.   D.

Difficulty: Medium

6. Which circle is divided into three equal shares?

A.   C.

B.   D.

Difficulty: Medium

7. Which circle is divided into three equal shares?

A.

B.

C.

D.

Difficulty: Medium

8. Which circle is divided into four equal shares?

A.

B.

C.

D.

Difficulty: Medium

9. Which circle is divided into four equal shares?

A.

B.

C.

D.

Difficulty: Medium

10. Which word most accurately describes one part of the following divided circle?

A. one-half
B. one-third
C. one
D. one-fourth

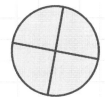

Difficulty: Medium

11. Which word most accurately describes one part of the following divided circle?

A. one-half
B. one-fourth
C. one-third
D. one

Difficulty: Medium

12. Which word most accurately describes one part of the following divided circle?

A. one
B. one-half
C. one-third
D. one-fourth

Difficulty: Medium

1. Explanation: If a shape is divided into 4 equal parts, each individual part would represent $\frac{1}{4}$ of the whole shape.

   The correct answer is C.

2. Explanation: If a shape is divided into 6 equal parts, each individual part would represent $\frac{1}{6}$ of the whole shape.

   The correct answer is D.

3. Explanation: If a shape is divided into 8 equal parts, each individual part would represent $\frac{1}{8}$ of the whole shape.

   The correct answer is C.

4. Explanation: This shape is the only one that contains a line that divides it into two smaller shapes of the same size.

   The correct answer is A.

5. Explanation: This shape is the only one that contains a line that divides it into two smaller shapes of the same size.

   The correct answer is C.

6. Explanation: This shape is the only one that contains lines that divide it into three smaller shapes of the same size.

   The correct answer is C.

7. Explanation: This shape is the only one that contains lines that divide it into three smaller shapes of the same size.

   The correct answer is C.

8. Explanation: This shape is the only one that contains lines that divide it into four smaller shapes of the same size.

   The correct answer is B.

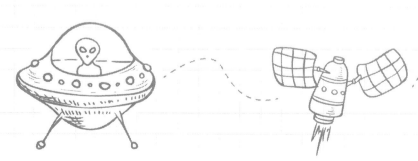

9. Explanation: This shape is the only one that contains lines that divide it into four smaller shapes of the same size.

   The correct answer is A.

11. Explanation: The circle is not divided into any parts. It is a whole circle, so the word that describes it is one.

    The correct answer is D.

10. Explanation: The circle is divided into four equal parts. Each part can be described as $\frac{1}{4}$ or one-fourth of the total circle.

    The correct answer is D.

12. Explanation: The circle is divided into two equal parts. Each part can be described as $\frac{1}{2}$ or one-half of the total circle.

    The correct answer is B.

1. Divide the circle into fourths.

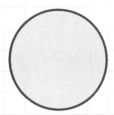

Difficulty: Medium

2. Which word is equivalent to the following fraction: $\frac{1}{2}$

A. Whole   C. Third
B. Half   D. Fourth

Difficulty: Medium

3. Which word is equivalent to the following fraction: $\frac{1}{4}$

A. Whole   C. Third
B. Half   D. Fourth

Difficulty: Medium

4. Which word is equivalent to the following fraction: $\frac{1}{3}$

A. Whole   C. Third
B. Half   D. Fourth

Difficulty: Medium

5. Which fraction is equivalent to a third?

A. $\frac{1}{3}$ C. $\frac{1}{4}$

B. $\frac{1}{2}$ D. $\frac{1}{8}$

Difficulty: Medium

6. Which fraction is equivalent to a fourth?

A. $\frac{1}{2}$ C. $\frac{1}{3}$

B. $\frac{1}{4}$ D. $\frac{1}{6}$

Difficulty: Medium

7. Which triangle is divided into equal parts?

A.   C.

B.   D.

Difficulty: Hard

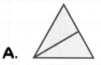

8. Which triangle is divided into equal parts?

A.

C.

B.

D.

Difficulty: Hard

9. Which pentagon is divided into equal parts?

A.

C.

B.

D.

Difficulty: Hard

10. Which pentagon is divided into equal parts?

A.

C.

B.

D.

Difficulty: Hard

11. Which shape is divided into equal parts?

A.

C.

B.

D.

Difficulty: Hard

12. Which shape is divided into equal parts?

A.

C.

B.

D.

Difficulty: Hard

13. Which fraction represents one part of the following shape?

A. $\dfrac{1}{4}$

C. $\dfrac{1}{2}$

B. $\dfrac{1}{3}$

D. $\dfrac{2}{1}$

Difficulty: Hard

1. Explanation: The circle is divided into four equal parts. Each part can be described as $\frac{1}{4}$ or one-fourth of the total circle.

   Students should draw two lines to divide the circle into four equal parts.

2. Explanation: The fraction $\frac{1}{2}$ is expressed by the words "one-half."

   The correct answer is B.

3. Explanation: The fraction $\frac{1}{4}$ is expressed by the words "one-fourth."

   The correct answer is D.

4. Explanation: The fraction $\frac{1}{3}$ is expressed by the words "one-third."

   The correct answer is C.

5. Explanation: The fraction $\frac{1}{3}$ is expressed by the words "one-third."

   The correct answer is A.

6. Explanation: The fraction $\frac{1}{4}$ is expressed by the words "one-fourth."

   The correct answer is B.

7. Explanation: This shape is the only one that contains a line that divides it into two smaller shapes of the same size.

   The correct answer is A.

8. Explanation: This shape is the only one that contains lines that divide it into four smaller shapes of the same size.

   The correct answer is A.

9. Explanation: This shape is the only one that contains a line that divides it into two smaller shapes of the same size.

   The correct answer is C.

10. Explanation: This shape is the only one that contains a line that divides it into five smaller shapes of the same size.

    The correct answer is D.

11. Explanation: This shape is the only one that contains a line that divides it into two smaller shapes of the same size.

    The correct answer is B.

12. Explanation: This shape is the only one that contains a line that divides it into two smaller shapes of the same size.

    The correct answer is A.

13. Explanation: This shape is divided into 4 equal parts. One part is represented by the 1 on top of the fraction and the four parts are represented by the four on the bottom of the fraction.

    The correct answer is A.

1. Which fraction represents one part of the following shape?

A. $\dfrac{2}{1}$ C. $\dfrac{1}{3}$

B. $\dfrac{1}{2}$ D. $\dfrac{1}{4}$

Difficulty: Hard

2. Divide the shape into equal parts.

Difficulty: Hard

3. Divide the shape into equal parts.

Difficulty: Hard

4. Which fraction would represent a shape divided into 7 equal parts?

A. $\dfrac{6}{1}$ C. $\dfrac{1}{7}$

B. $\dfrac{1}{8}$ D. $\dfrac{7}{1}$

Difficulty: Hard

5. Which fraction would represent a shape divided into 10 equal parts?

A. $\dfrac{5}{2}$ C. $\dfrac{10}{1}$

B. $\dfrac{1}{10}$ D. $\dfrac{2}{5}$

Difficulty: Hard

6. Which fraction would represent a shape divided into 11 equal parts?

A. $\dfrac{2}{9}$ C. $\dfrac{11}{1}$

B. $\dfrac{1}{11}$ D. $\dfrac{5}{6}$

Difficulty: Hard

7. Which fraction would represent a shape divided into 9 equal parts?

A. $\dfrac{1}{9}$ C. $\dfrac{1}{10}$

B. $\dfrac{9}{1}$ D. $\dfrac{11}{1}$

Difficulty: Hard

8. Which fraction would represent a shape divided into 12 equal parts?

A. $\dfrac{1}{3}$ C. $\dfrac{12}{1}$

B. $\dfrac{1}{4}$ D. $\dfrac{1}{12}$

Difficulty: Hard

1. Explanation: This shape is divided into 2 equal parts. One part is represented by the I on top of the fraction and the two parts are represented by the two on the bottom of the fraction.

   The correct answer is B.

2. Explanation: To divide a shape into equal parts, you should draw a line that keeps each smaller part equal to all the other parts.

   Students should draw at least one line that divides the shape into equal parts.

3. Explanation: To divide a shape into equal parts, you should draw a line that keeps each smaller part equal to all the other parts.

   Students should draw at least one line that divides the shape into equal parts.

4. Explanation: When a shape is divided into equal parts, the number of the parts is equal to the denominator of the fraction.

   The correct answer is C.

5. Explanation: When a shape is divided into equal parts, the number of the parts is equal to the denominator of the fraction.

   The correct answer is B.

6. Explanation: When a shape is divided into equal parts, the number of the parts is equal to the denominator of the fraction.

   The correct answer is B.

7. Explanation: When a shape is divided into equal parts, the number of the parts is equal to the denominator of the fraction.

   The correct answer is A.

8. Explanation: When a shape is divided into equal parts, the number of the parts is equal to the denominator of the fraction.

   The correct answer is D.

✸ Numbers and Operations in Base Ten ✸
✸ Understanding Fractions ✸

1. What is the value of the numerator of this fraction: $\frac{5}{8}$

A. 2   C. 5

B. 3   D. 8

Difficulty: Hard

2. What is the value of the numerator of this fraction: $\frac{2}{3}$

A. 4   C. 3

B. 1   D. 2

Difficulty: Hard

3. What is the value of the numerator of this fraction: $\frac{3}{4}$

A. 3   C. 2

B. 4   D. 1

Difficulty: Hard

4. What is the value of the numerator of this fraction: $\frac{7}{9}$

A. 7   C. 9

B. 8   D. 10

Difficulty: Hard

5. What is the value of the numerator of this fraction: $\frac{6}{10}$

A. 4   C. 8

B. 6   D. 10

Difficulty: Hard

6. What is the value of the numerator of this fraction: $\frac{2}{7}$

A. 4   C. 2

B. 3   D. 1

Difficulty: Hard

7. What is the value of the denominator of this fraction: $\frac{5}{11}$

A. 2   C. 5

B. 3   D. 11

Difficulty: Hard

8. What is the value of the denominator of this fraction: $\frac{1}{4}$

A. 1   C. 2

B. 4   D. 3

Difficulty: Hard

9. What is the value of the denominator of this fraction: $\frac{5}{7}$

A. 7   **C.** 5
B. 6   **D.** 4

Difficulty: Hard

10. What is the value of the denominator of this fraction: $\frac{10}{12}$

A. 6   **C.** 12
B. 8   **D.** 10

Difficulty: Hard

11. What is the value of the denominator of this fraction: $\frac{2}{5}$

A. 6   **C.** 4
B. 5   **D.** 3

Difficulty: Hard

12. What is the value of the denominator of this fraction: $\frac{8}{9}$

A. 6   **C.** 8
B. 7   **D.** 9

Difficulty: Hard

13. Which fraction will take the place of the dot in the following number line?

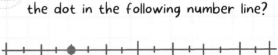

A. $\frac{1}{2}$ **C.** $\frac{1}{4}$
B. $\frac{3}{4}$ **D.** $\frac{1}{8}$

Difficulty: Hard

14. Which fraction will take the place of the dot in the following number line?

A. $\frac{1}{8}$ **C.** $\frac{1}{4}$
B. $\frac{1}{6}$ **D.** $\frac{1}{2}$

Difficulty: Hard

15. Which fraction will take the place of the dot in the following number line?

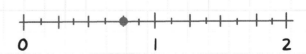

A. $\frac{1}{4}$ **C.** $\frac{3}{4}$
B. $\frac{1}{2}$ **D.** $\frac{1}{3}$

Difficulty: Hard

1. Explanation: The numerator of a fraction is the value of the top part of the fraction.

   The correct answer is C.

2. Explanation: The numerator of a fraction is the value of the top part of the fraction.

   The correct answer is D.

3. Explanation: The numerator of a fraction is the value of the top part of the fraction.

   The correct answer is A.

4. Explanation: The numerator of a fraction is the value of the top part of the fraction.

   The correct answer is A.

5. Explanation: The numerator of a fraction is the value of the top part of the fraction.

   The correct answer is B.

6. Explanation: The numerator of a fraction is the value of the top part of the fraction.

   The correct answer is C.

7. Explanation: The denominator of a fraction is the value of the bottom part of the fraction.

   The correct answer is D.

8. Explanation: The denominator of a fraction is the value of the bottom part of the fraction.

   The correct answer is B.

9. Explanation: The denominator of a fraction is the value of the bottom part of the fraction.

The correct answer is A.

10. Explanation: The denominator of a fraction is the value of the bottom part of the fraction.

The correct answer is C.

11. Explanation: The denominator of a fraction is the value of the bottom part of the fraction.

The correct answer is B.

12. Explanation: The denominator of a fraction is the value of the bottom part of the fraction.

The correct answer is D.

13. Explanation: The dot marks the part on the line where the line can be divided into two equal parts.

The correct answer is A.

14. Explanation: The dot marks the first part on the line where the line can be divided into eight equal parts.

The correct answer is A.

15. Explanation: The dot marks the third part on the line where the line can be divided into four equal parts.

The correct answer is C.

1. Which fraction will take the place of the dot in the following number line?

A. $\frac{1}{8}$ C. $\frac{6}{8}$

B. $\frac{7}{8}$ D. $\frac{3}{4}$

Difficulty: Hard

2. Which fraction will take the place of the dot in the following number line?

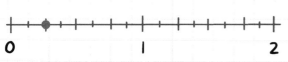

A. $\frac{2}{1}$ C. $\frac{1}{3}$

B. $\frac{1}{2}$ D. $\frac{1}{4}$

Difficulty: Hard

3. Which shape could also represent $\frac{1}{2}$?

A.   C.

B.   D.

Difficulty: Hard

4. Which shape could also represent $\frac{1}{4}$?

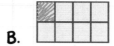 

A.   C.

B.   D.

Difficulty: Hard

5. Which fraction could also take the place of $\frac{6}{8}$ on the number line?

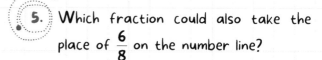

A. $\frac{3}{4}$ C. $\frac{1}{4}$

B. $\frac{1}{2}$ D. $\frac{3}{2}$

Difficulty: Hard

6. Which fraction could also take the place of $\frac{4}{8}$ on the number line?

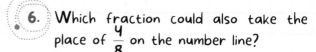

A. $\frac{2}{4}$ C. $\frac{1}{4}$

B. $\frac{1}{3}$ D. $\frac{3}{4}$

Difficulty: Hard

1. Explanation: The dot marks the seventh part on the line where the line can be divided into eight equal parts.

   The correct answer is B.

2. Explanation: The dot marks the first part on the line where the line can be divided into four equal parts.

   The correct answer is D.

3. Explanation: The filled parts of D represent $\frac{2}{4}$ of the circle, but could also represent $\frac{1}{2}$.

   The correct answer is D.

4. Explanation: The filled parts of C represent $\frac{2}{8}$ of the rectangle but could also represent $\frac{1}{4}$.

   The correct answer is C.

5. Explanation: The line for $\frac{6}{8}$ on the number is also equal to $\frac{3}{4}$.

   The correct answer is A.

6. Explanation: The line for $\frac{4}{8}$ on the number line is also equal to $\frac{2}{4}$.

   The correct answer is A.

1. Which fraction represents the unit fraction of the following shape?

A. $\frac{1}{6}$ C. $\frac{1}{4}$

B. $\frac{1}{8}$ D. $\frac{1}{2}$

Difficulty: Hard

2. Which fraction represents the unit fraction of the following shape?

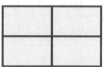

A. $\frac{1}{2}$ C. $\frac{1}{4}$

B. $\frac{1}{3}$ D. $\frac{1}{5}$

Difficulty: Hard

3. Which fraction represents the unit fraction of the following shape?

A. $\frac{3}{1}$ C. $\frac{1}{3}$

B. $\frac{1}{2}$ D. $\frac{1}{4}$

Difficulty: Hard

4. Which fraction represents the unit fraction of the following shape?

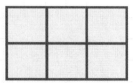

A. $\frac{1}{6}$ C. $\frac{1}{4}$

B. $\frac{1}{5}$ D. $\frac{1}{3}$

Difficulty: Hard

5. If the unit fraction is $\frac{1}{5}$, how many parts would the shape be divided into?

A. 6   C. 3

B. 1   D. 5

Difficulty: Hard

6. If the unit fraction is $\frac{1}{2}$, how many parts would the shape be divided into?

A. 2   C. 4

B. 1   D. 3

Difficulty: Hard

7. If the unit fraction is $\frac{1}{7}$, how many parts would the shape be divided into?

A. 1

B. 7

C. 2

D. 3

Difficulty: Hard

8. What would be the numerator of the unit fraction expressed by the following shape?

A. 1

B. 2

C. 3

D. 4

Difficulty: Hard

9. What would be the denominator of the unit fraction expressed by the following shape?

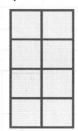

A. 3

B. 3

C. 8

D. 6

Difficulty: Hard

10. What would be the denominator of the unit fraction expressed by the following shape?

A. 4

B. 3

C. 2

D. 1

Difficulty: Hard

11. What would be the denominator of the unit fraction expressed by the following shape?

A. 1

B. 2

C. 3

D. 5

Difficulty: Hard

12. What is the unit fraction that makes up $\frac{4}{7}$?

A. $\frac{1}{4}$

B. $\frac{1}{7}$

C. $\frac{4}{1}$

D. $\frac{7}{1}$

Difficulty: Hard

1. Explanation: The circle is divided into 8 equal parts. The unit fraction can be represented as $\frac{1}{8}$.

   The correct answer is B.

2. Explanation: The rectangle is divided into 4 equal parts. The unit fraction can be represented as $\frac{1}{4}$.

   The correct answer is C.

3. Explanation: The rectangle is divided into 3 equal parts. The unit fraction can be represented as $\frac{1}{3}$.

   The correct answer is C.

4. Explanation: The rectangle is divided into 6 equal parts. The unit fraction can be represented as $\frac{1}{6}$.

   The correct answer is A.

5. Explanation: The unit fraction represents one part of the shape. The denominator of a unit fraction can show you how many parts a shape is divided into.

   The correct answer is D.

6. Explanation: The unit fraction represents one part of the shape. The denominator of a unit fraction can show you how many parts a shape is divided into.

   The correct answer is A.

7. Explanation: The unit fraction represents one part of the shape. The denominator of a unit fraction can show you how many parts a shape is divided into.

   The correct answer is B.

8. Explanation: The circle is divided into 3 equal parts. The unit fraction can be represented as $\frac{1}{3}$. The numerator of the unit fraction is 1.

   The correct answer is A.

9. Explanation: The rectangle is divided into 8 equal parts. The unit fraction can be represented as $\frac{1}{8}$. The denominator of the unit fraction is 8.

   The correct answer is C.

10. Explanation: The circle is divided into 4 equal parts. The unit fraction can be represented as $\frac{1}{4}$. The denominator of the unit fraction is 4.

    The correct answer is A.

11. Explanation: The pentagon is divided into 5 equal parts. The unit fraction can be represented as $\frac{1}{5}$. The denominator of the unit fraction is 5.

    The correct answer is D.

12. Explanation: The numerator of a unit fraction is always 1. The denominator of a unit fraction can show you how many parts a shape is divided into.

    Correct answer: B.

1. What is the unit fraction that makes up $\frac{9}{12}$?

A. $\frac{1}{12}$ **C.** $\frac{9}{1}$

B. $\frac{1}{9}$ **D.** $\frac{12}{1}$

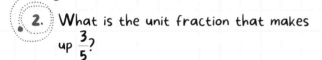
Difficulty: Hard

2. What is the unit fraction that makes up $\frac{3}{5}$?

A. $\frac{1}{9}$ **C.** $\frac{1}{3}$

B. $\frac{1}{8}$ **D.** $\frac{1}{5}$

Difficulty: Hard

3. Draw a shape and represent the unit fraction $\frac{1}{8}$.

Difficulty: Hard

4. Draw a shape and represent the unit fraction $\frac{1}{6}$.

Difficulty: Hard

5. Draw a shape and represent the fraction $\frac{1}{10}$.

Difficulty: Hard

6. Which number should replace the ? to make the fraction equal?

$$\frac{3}{4} = \frac{?}{12}$$

A. 6   **C.** 9

B. 8   **D.** 10

Difficulty: Hard

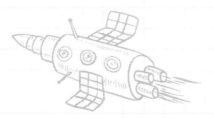

7. Which number should replace the ? to make the fraction equal?

$$\frac{?}{9} = \frac{2}{3}$$

A. 3   C. 5

B. 4   D. 6

Difficulty: Hard

8. Which number should replace the ? to make the fraction equal?

$$\frac{2}{4} = \frac{?}{2}$$

A. 4   C. 2

B. 1   D. 3

Difficulty: Hard

9. Which number should replace the ? to make the fraction equal?

$$\frac{2}{8} = \frac{1}{?}$$

A. 5   C. 3

B. 4   D. 2

Difficulty: Hard

10. Which number should replace the ? to make the fraction equal?

$$\frac{?}{3} = \frac{2}{6}$$

A. 1   C. 3

B. 2   D. 4

Difficulty: Hard

11. Which number should replace the ? to make the fraction equal?

$$\frac{1}{?} = \frac{6}{12}$$

A. 2   C. 4

B. 3   D. 5

Difficulty: Hard

12. Which number should replace the ? to make the fraction equal?

$$\frac{1}{5} = \frac{?}{10}$$

A. 5   C. 3

B. 4   D. 2

Difficulty: Hard

13. Which number should replace the ? to make the fraction equal?

$$\frac{1}{3} = \frac{4}{?}$$

A. 15   C. 12

B. 9   D. 16

Difficulty: Hard

1. Explanation: The numerator of a unit fraction is always 1. The denominator of a unit fraction can show you how many parts a shape is divided into.

   Correct answer: A.

2. Explanation: The numerator of a unit fraction is always 1. The denominator of a unit fraction can show you how many parts a shape is divided into.

   Correct answer: D.

3. Explanation: A unit fraction can represent one smaller part of the fraction division. In this case, you should divide the shape into eight equal parts and then shade one part.

   Students should draw a shape and divide it into eight parts. Students should shade 1 part.

4. Explanation: A unit fraction can represent one smaller part of the fraction division. In this case, you should divide the shape into six equal parts and then shade one part.

   Students should draw a shape and divide it into six parts. Students should shade 1 part.

5. Explanation: A unit fraction can represent one smaller part of the fraction division. In this case, you should divide the shape into ten equal parts and then shade one part.

   Students should draw a shape and divide it into ten parts. Students should shade 1 part.

6. Explanation: Think about a rectangle that is divided into four parts. If you color three of the parts, it would be the same as if you divided a rectangle into twelve parts and colored nine.

   The correct answer is C.

7. Explanation: Think about a circle that is divided into nine parts. If you color six of the parts, it would be the same as if you divided a circle into three parts and colored two.

The correct answer is D.

8. Explanation: Think about a circle that is divided into four parts. If you color two of the parts, it would be the same as if you divided a circle into two parts and colored one.

The correct answer is B.

9. Explanation: Think about a rectangle that is divided into eight parts. If you color **2** of the parts, it would be the same as if you divided a rectangle into four parts and colored one.

The correct answer is B.

10. Explanation: Think about a circle that is divided into six parts. If you color **2** of the parts, it would be the same as if you divided a circle into three parts and colored one.

The correct answer is A.

11. Explanation: Think about a rectangle that is divided into two parts. If you color 1 of the parts, it would be the same as if you divided a rectangle into twelve parts and colored six.

The correct answer is A.

12. Explanation: Think about a rectangle that is divided into five parts. If you color 1 of the parts, it would be the same as if you divided a rectangle into ten parts and colored two.

The correct answer is D.

13. Explanation: Think about a circle that is divided into three parts. If you color 1 of the parts, it would be the same as if you divided a circle into twelve parts and colored four.

The correct answer is C.

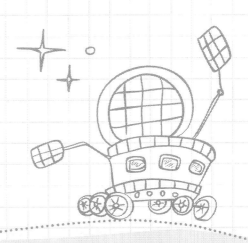

1. Which number should replace the ? to make the fraction equal?

$$\frac{?}{16} = \frac{1}{4}$$

A. 1   C. 4

B. 2   D. 6

Difficulty: Hard

2. Which number should replace the ? to make the fraction equal?

$$\frac{2}{?} = \frac{1}{6}$$

A. 10   C. 14

B. 12   D. 16

Difficulty: Hard

3. Which number should replace the ? to make the fraction equal?

$$\frac{1}{6} = \frac{5}{?}$$

A. 30   C. 20

B. 25   D. 15

Difficulty: Hard

4. Which number should replace the ? to make the fraction equal?

$$\frac{5}{15} = \frac{?}{3}$$

A. 3   C. 1

B. 2   D. 4

Difficulty: Hard

5. Which number should replace the ? to make the fraction equal?

$$\frac{4}{16} = \frac{1}{?}$$

A. 1   C. 3

B. 2   D. 4

Difficulty: Hard

6. Which fraction is a whole number?

A. $\frac{1}{2}$ C. $\frac{2}{3}$

B. $\frac{2}{2}$ D. $\frac{3}{7}$

Difficulty: Hard

7. Which fraction is a whole number?

A. $\frac{3}{3}$ C. $\frac{3}{1}$

B. $\frac{1}{3}$ D. $\frac{2}{3}$

Difficulty: Hard

8. Which fraction is a whole number?

A. $\frac{1}{4}$ C. $\frac{3}{4}$

B. $\frac{2}{4}$ D. $\frac{4}{4}$

Difficulty: Hard

9. Which fraction is a whole number?

A. $\dfrac{6}{1}$ C. $\dfrac{1}{6}$

B. $\dfrac{6}{6}$ D. $\dfrac{2}{3}$

Difficulty: Hard

10. Which fraction is a whole number?

A. $\dfrac{11}{11}$ C. $\dfrac{11}{1}$

B. $\dfrac{1}{11}$ D. $\dfrac{5}{6}$

Difficulty: Hard

11. Which fraction is a whole number?

A. $\dfrac{24}{1}$ C. $\dfrac{24}{24}$

B. $\dfrac{1}{24}$ D. $\dfrac{12}{24}$

Difficulty: Hard

12. Which fraction is equal to 1?

A. $\dfrac{3}{1}$ C. $\dfrac{5}{5}$

B. $\dfrac{3}{5}$ D. $\dfrac{5}{7}$

Difficulty: Hard

13. Which fraction is equal to 1?

A. $\dfrac{2}{4}$ C. $\dfrac{4}{2}$

B. $\dfrac{4}{4}$ D. $\dfrac{1}{2}$

Difficulty: Hard

14. Which fraction is equal to 1?

A. $\dfrac{3}{3}$ C. $\dfrac{3}{7}$

B. $\dfrac{3}{2}$ D. $\dfrac{7}{3}$

Difficulty: Hard

15. Which fraction is equal to 1?

A. $\dfrac{2}{1}$ C. $\dfrac{2}{4}$

B. $\dfrac{1}{2}$ D. $\dfrac{2}{2}$

Difficulty: Hard

16. Which fraction is equal to 1?

A. $\dfrac{10}{10}$ C. $\dfrac{1}{10}$

B. $\dfrac{10}{1}$ D. $\dfrac{5}{10}$

Difficulty: Hard

1. Explanation: Think about a rectangle that is divided into four parts. If you color 1 of the parts, it would be the same as if you divided a rectangle into sixteen parts and colored four.

   The correct answer is C.

2. Explanation: Think about a circle that is divided into six parts. If you color 1 of the parts, it would be the same as if you divided a circle into twelve parts and colored two.

   The correct answer is B.

3. Explanation: Think about a circle that is divided into six parts. If you color 1 of the parts, it would be the same as if you divided a circle into thirty parts and colored five.

   The correct answer is A.

4. Explanation: Think about a circle that is divided into fifteen parts. If you color 5 of the parts, it would be the same as if you divided a circle into three parts and colored one.

   The correct answer is C.

5. Explanation: Think about a circle that is divided into sixteen parts. If you color 4 of the parts, it would be the same as if you divided a circle into four parts and colored one.

   The correct answer is D.

6. Explanation: A fraction with an equal numerator and denominator is equivalent to 1.

   The correct answer is B.

7. Explanation: A fraction with an equal numerator and denominator is equivalent to 1.

   The correct answer is A.

8. Explanation: A fraction with an equal numerator and denominator is equivalent to 1.

The correct answer is D.

9. Explanation : A fraction with an equal numerator and denominator is equivalent to 1.

The correct answer is B.

10. Explanation: A fraction with an equal numerator and denominator is equivalent to 1.

The correct answer is A.

11. Explanation: A fraction with an equal numerator and denominator is equivalent to 1.

The correct answer is C.

12. Explanation: A fraction with an equal numerator and denominator is equivalent to 1.

The correct answer is C.

13. Explanation: A fraction with an equal numerator and denominator is equivalent to 1.

The correct answer is B.

14. Explanation: A fraction with an equal numerator and denominator is equivalent to 1.

The correct answer is A.

15. Explanation: A fraction with an equal numerator and denominator is equivalent to 1.

The correct answer is D.

16. Explanation: A fraction with an equal numerator and denominator is equivalent to 1.

The correct answer is A.

1. Which fraction is equal to 1?

   A. $\frac{12}{12}$ C. $\frac{12}{1}$

   B. $\frac{6}{12}$ D. $\frac{1}{12}$

   Difficulty: Hard

2. Which number should be placed in the numerator of the following fraction, to make it equal to 1?

   $$\frac{?}{5}$$

   A. 5   C. 3

   B. 4   D. 2

   Difficulty: Hard

3. Which number should be placed in the numerator of the following fraction, to make it equal to 1?

   $$\frac{?}{10}$$

   A. 6   C. 10

   B. 8   D. 12

   Difficulty: Hard

4. Which number should be placed in the numerator of the following fraction, to make it greater than 1?

   $$\frac{?}{50}$$

   A. 30   C. 50

   B. 60   D. 10

   Difficulty: Hard

5. Which number should be placed in the numerator of the following fraction, to make it greater than 1?

   $$\frac{?}{7}$$

   A. 5   C. 7

   B. 6   D. 8

   Difficulty: Hard

6. Which number should be placed in the denominator of the following fraction, to make it equal to 1?

   $$\frac{6}{?}$$

   A. 3   C. 5

   B. 4   D. 6

   Difficulty: Hard

7. Which number should be placed in the denominator of the following fraction, to make it equal to 1?

$$\frac{11}{?}$$

A. 10   C. 12

B. 11   D. 13

Difficulty: Hard

8. Which number should be placed in the denominator of the following fraction, to make it greater than 1?

$$\frac{25}{?}$$

A. 20   C. 30

B. 25   D. 35

Difficulty: Hard

9. Which number should be placed in the denominator of the following fraction, to make it greater than 1?

$$\frac{10}{?}$$

A. 11   C. 10

B. 9   D. 20

Difficulty: Hard

1. Explanation: A fraction with an equal numerator and denominator is equivalent to 1.

   The correct answer is A.

2. Explanation: A fraction with an equal numerator and denominator is equivalent to 1.

   The correct answer is A.

3. Explanation: A fraction with an equal numerator and denominator is equivalent to 1.

   The correct answer is C.

4. Explanation: A fraction with an equal numerator and denominator is equivalent to 1. Any fraction that has a larger numerator than denominator will be greater than 1.

   The correct answer is B.

5. Explanation: A fraction with an equal numerator and denominator is equivalent to 1. Any fraction that has a larger numerator than denominator will be greater than 1.

   The correct answer is D.

6. Explanation: A fraction with an equal numerator and denominator is equivalent to 1.

   The correct answer is D.

7. Explanation: A fraction with an equal numerator and denominator is equivalent to 1.

   The correct answer is B.

8. Explanation: A fraction with an equal numerator and denominator is equivalent to 1. Any fraction that has a larger numerator than denominator will be greater than 1.

   The correct answer is A.

9. Explanation: A fraction with an equal numerator and denominator is equivalent to 1. Any fraction that has a larger numerator than denominator will be greater than 1.

   The correct answer is B.

1. Which fraction is largest?

A. $\dfrac{1}{2}$ C. $\dfrac{1}{4}$

B. $\dfrac{1}{3}$ D. $\dfrac{1}{6}$

Difficulty: Hard

2. Which fraction is largest?

A. $\dfrac{4}{8}$ C. $\dfrac{4}{14}$

B. $\dfrac{4}{12}$ D. $\dfrac{4}{16}$

Difficulty: Hard

3. Which fraction is largest?

A. $\dfrac{7}{15}$ C. $\dfrac{7}{11}$

B. $\dfrac{7}{13}$ D. $\dfrac{7}{9}$

Difficulty: Hard

4. Which fraction is largest?

A. $\dfrac{2}{20}$ C. $\dfrac{2}{10}$

B. $\dfrac{2}{18}$ D. $\dfrac{2}{9}$

Difficulty: Hard

5. Which fraction is largest?

A. $\dfrac{5}{11}$ C. $\dfrac{5}{10}$

B. $\dfrac{5}{8}$ D. $\dfrac{5}{9}$

Difficulty: Hard

6. Which fraction is smallest?

A. $\dfrac{2}{3}$ C. $\dfrac{2}{6}$

B. $\dfrac{2}{4}$ D. $\dfrac{2}{8}$

Difficulty: Hard

7. Which fraction is smallest?

A. $\dfrac{3}{10}$ C. $\dfrac{3}{20}$

B. $\dfrac{3}{15}$ D. $\dfrac{3}{25}$

Difficulty: Hard

8. Which fraction is smallest?

A. $\dfrac{5}{15}$ C. $\dfrac{5}{25}$

B. $\dfrac{5}{20}$ D. $\dfrac{5}{30}$

Difficulty: Hard

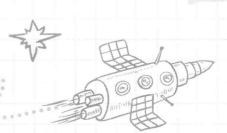

9. Which fraction is smallest?

A. $\frac{6}{20}$ C. $\frac{6}{16}$

B. $\frac{6}{24}$ D. $\frac{6}{10}$

Difficulty: Hard

10. Which fraction is smallest?

A. $\frac{1}{15}$ C. $\frac{1}{24}$

B. $\frac{1}{18}$ D. $\frac{1}{22}$

Difficulty: Hard

11. Which fraction is smallest?

A. $\frac{4}{5}$ C. $\frac{4}{7}$

B. $\frac{4}{6}$ D. $\frac{4}{8}$

Difficulty: Hard

12. Place <, >, or = to make the comparison correct:

$$\frac{4}{6} \rule{2cm}{0.4pt} \frac{4}{5}$$

Difficulty: Hard

13. Place <, >, or = to make the comparison correct:

$$\frac{2}{6} \rule{2cm}{0.4pt} \frac{2}{3}$$

Difficulty: Hard

14. Place <, >, or = to make the comparison correct:

$$\frac{4}{5} \rule{2cm}{0.4pt} \frac{4}{8}$$

Difficulty: Hard

15. Place <, >, or = to make the comparison correct:

$$\frac{3}{9} \rule{2cm}{0.4pt} \frac{3}{5}$$

Difficulty: Hard

16. Place <, >, or = to make the comparison correct:

$$\frac{6}{7} \rule{2cm}{0.4pt} \frac{6}{10}$$

Difficulty: Hard

17. Place <, >, or = to make the comparison correct:

$$\frac{11}{15} \rule{2cm}{0.4pt} \frac{11}{20}$$

Difficulty: Hard

1. Explanation: When comparing fractions with the same numerator, the larger the denominator, the smaller the fraction.

   The correct answer is A.

2. Explanation: When comparing fractions with the same numerator, the larger the denominator, the smaller the fraction.

   The correct answer is A.

3. Explanation: When comparing fractions with the same numerator, the larger the denominator, the smaller the fraction.

   The correct answer is D.

4. Explanation: When comparing fractions with the same numerator, the larger the denominator, the smaller the fraction.

   The correct answer is D.

5. Explanation: When comparing fractions with the same numerator, the larger the denominator, the smaller the fraction.

   The correct answer is B.

6. Explanation: When comparing fractions with the same numerator, the larger the denominator, the smaller the fraction.

   The correct answer is D.

7. Explanation: When comparing fractions with the same numerator, the larger the denominator, the smaller the fraction.

   The correct answer is D.

8. Explanation: When comparing fractions with the same numerator, the larger the denominator, the smaller the fraction.

   The correct answer is D.

9. Explanation: When comparing fractions with the same numerator, the larger the denominator, the smaller the fraction.

   The correct answer is B.

10. Explanation: When comparing fractions with the same numerator, the larger the denominator, the smaller the fraction.

    The correct answer is C.

11. Explanation: When comparing fractions with the same numerator, the larger the denominator, the smaller the fraction.

    The correct answer is D.

12. Explanation: When comparing fractions with the same numerator, the larger the denominator, the smaller the fraction.

    The correct answer is <.

13. Explanation: When comparing fractions with the same numerator, the larger the denominator, the smaller the fraction.

    The correct answer is <.

14. Explanation: When comparing fractions with the same numerator, the larger the denominator, the smaller the fraction.

    The correct answer is >.

15. Explanation: When comparing fractions with the same numerator, the larger the denominator, the smaller the fraction.

    The correct answer is <.

16. Explanation: When comparing fractions with the same numerator, the larger the denominator, the smaller the fraction.

    The correct answer is >.

17. Explanation: When comparing fractions with the same numerator, the larger the denominator, the smaller the fraction.

    The correct answer is >.

1. Place <, >, or = to make the comparison correct:

$$\frac{9}{11} \qquad \frac{9}{10}$$

Difficulty: Hard

2. Which fraction is the largest?

A. $\frac{4}{5}$

B. $\frac{3}{5}$

C. $\frac{2}{5}$

D. $\frac{1}{5}$

Difficulty: Hard

3. Which fraction is the largest?

A. $\frac{1}{8}$

B. $\frac{2}{8}$

C. $\frac{4}{8}$

D. $\frac{6}{8}$

Difficulty: Hard

4. Which fraction is the largest?

A. $\frac{2}{12}$

B. $\frac{4}{12}$

C. $\frac{9}{12}$

D. $\frac{6}{12}$

Difficulty: Hard

5. Which fraction is the largest?

A. $\frac{4}{4}$

B. $\frac{3}{4}$

C. $\frac{2}{4}$

D. $\frac{1}{4}$

Difficulty: Hard

6. Which fraction is the largest?

A. $\frac{2}{6}$

B. $\frac{3}{6}$

C. $\frac{4}{6}$

D. $\frac{5}{6}$

Difficulty: Hard

7. Which fraction is the largest?

A. $\frac{3}{7}$

B. $\frac{5}{7}$

C. $\frac{2}{7}$

D. $\frac{4}{7}$

Difficulty: Hard

8. Which fraction is the smallest?

A. $\frac{4}{9}$ C. $\frac{3}{9}$

B. $\frac{5}{9}$ D. $\frac{6}{9}$

Difficulty: Hard

9. Which fraction is the smallest?

A. $\frac{10}{20}$ C. $\frac{12}{20}$

B. $\frac{8}{20}$ D. $\frac{14}{20}$

Difficulty: Hard

10. Which fraction is the smallest?

A. $\frac{6}{12}$ C. $\frac{7}{12}$

B. $\frac{5}{12}$ D. $\frac{9}{12}$

Difficulty: Hard

11. Which fraction is the smallest?

A. $\frac{1}{20}$ C. $\frac{5}{20}$

B. $\frac{3}{20}$ D. $\frac{19}{20}$

Difficulty: Hard

12. Which fraction is the smallest?

A. $\frac{4}{5}$ C. $\frac{6}{5}$

B. $\frac{5}{5}$ D. $\frac{7}{5}$

Difficulty: Hard

13. Which fraction is the smallest?

A. $\frac{20}{25}$ C. $\frac{10}{25}$

B. $\frac{15}{25}$ D. $\frac{5}{25}$

Difficulty: Hard

14. Place <, >, or = to make the comparison correct:

$$\frac{7}{9} \sim\sim\sim \frac{4}{9}$$

Difficulty: Hard

15. Place <, >, or = to make the comparison correct:

$$\frac{2}{5} \sim\sim\sim \frac{4}{5}$$

Difficulty: Hard

16. Place <, >, or = to make the comparison correct:

$$\frac{6}{7} \sim\sim\sim \frac{2}{7}$$

Difficulty: Hard

17. Place <, >, or = to make the comparison correct:

$$\frac{2}{3} \sim\sim\sim \frac{1}{3}$$

Difficulty: Hard

18. Place <, >, or = to make the comparison correct:

$$\frac{1}{4} \sim\sim\sim \frac{3}{4}$$

Difficulty: Hard

19. Place <, >, or = to make the comparison correct:

$$\frac{5}{6} \sim\sim\sim \frac{1}{6}$$

Difficulty: Hard

20. Place <, >, or = to make the comparison correct:

$$\frac{1}{10} \sim\sim\sim \frac{2}{10}$$

Difficulty: Hard

1. Explanation: When comparing fractions with the same numerator, the larger the denominator, the smaller the fraction.

   The correct answer is <.

2. Explanation: When comparing fractions with the same denominator, the larger the numerator, the larger the fraction.

   The correct answer is A.

3. Explanation: When comparing fractions with the same denominator, the larger the numerator, the larger the fraction.

   The correct answer is D.

4. Explanation: When comparing fractions with the same denominator, the larger the numerator, the larger the fraction.

   The correct answer is C.

5. Explanation: When comparing fractions with the same denominator, the larger the numerator, the larger the fraction.

   The correct answer is A.

6. Explanation: When comparing fractions with the same denominator, the larger the numerator, the larger the fraction.

   The correct answer is D.

7. Explanation: When comparing fractions with the same denominator, the larger the numerator, the larger the fraction.

   The correct answer is B.

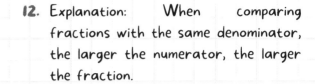

8. Explanation: When comparing fractions with the same denominator, the larger the numerator, the larger the fraction.

   The correct answer is C.

9. Explanation: When comparing fractions with the same denominator, the larger the numerator, the larger the fraction.

   The correct answer is B.

10. Explanation: When comparing fractions with the same denominator, the larger the numerator, the larger the fraction.

    The correct answer is B.

11. Explanation: When comparing fractions with the same denominator, the larger the numerator, the larger the fraction.

    The correct answer is A.

12. Explanation: When comparing fractions with the same denominator, the larger the numerator, the larger the fraction.

    The correct answer is A.

13. Explanation: When comparing fractions with the same denominator, the larger the numerator, the larger the fraction.

    The correct answer is D.

14. Explanation: When comparing fractions with the same denominator, the larger the numerator, the larger the fraction.

    The correct answer is >.

15. Explanation: When comparing fractions with the same denominator, the larger the numerator, the larger the fraction.

The correct answer is <.

16. Explanation: When comparing fractions with the same denominator, the larger the numerator, the larger the fraction.

The correct answer is >.

17. Explanation: When comparing fractions with the same denominator, the larger the numerator, the larger the fraction.

The correct answer is >.

18. Explanation: When comparing fractions with the same denominator, the larger the numerator, the larger the fraction.

The correct answer is <.

19. Explanation: When comparing fractions with the same denominator, the larger the numerator, the larger the fraction.

The correct answer is >.

20. Explanation: When comparing fractions with the same denominator, the larger the numerator, the larger the fraction.

The correct answer is <.

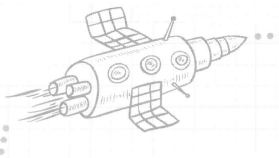

Measurement and Data

1. **Measurement of Objects** page 168

2. **Area and Perimeter** page 191

3. **Measurement of Time** page 202

4. **Measurement of Data** page 210

5. **Measurement word problems** page 215

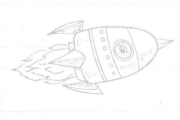

1. Which object is the longest?

A.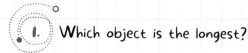

B.

C.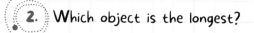

D.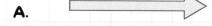

Difficulty: Easy

2. Which object is the longest?

A.

B.

C.

D.

Difficulty: Easy

3. Which object is the shortest?

A. B. C. D.

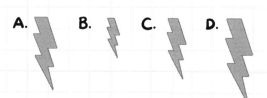

Difficulty: Easy

4. Which object is the shortest?

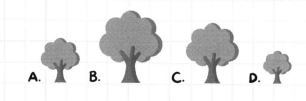
A.   B.   C.   D.

Difficulty: Easy

5. Which item is the widest?

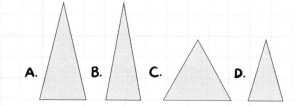
A.   B.   C.   D.

Difficulty: Easy

6. Which item is the widest?

A. B. C. D.

Difficulty: Easy

7. Which item is the skinniest?

A. B. C. D.

Difficulty: Easy

8. Which item is the skinniest?

A. B. C. D.

Difficulty: Easy

9. Which object is as long as the arrow?

A.

B.

C.

D.

Difficulty: Easy

10. Which object is as long as the arrow?

A.

B.

C.

D.

Difficulty: Easy

11. Which object is longer than the arrow?

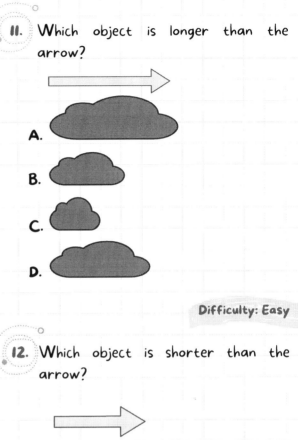

A.

B.

C.

D.

Difficulty: Easy

12. Which object is shorter than the arrow?

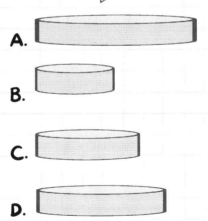

A.

B.

C.

D.

Difficulty: Easy

1. Explanation: Choice D is the longest caterpillar as it takes up the most space from left to right.

   The correct answer is D.

2. Explanation: Object A is the longest as it takes up the most space from left to right.

   The correct answer is A.

3. Explanation: Choice B is the shortest as it takes up the least space from top to bottom.

   The correct answer is B.

4. Explanation: Choice D is the shortest as it takes up the least space from top to bottom.

   The correct answer is D.

5. Explanation: Choice C is the widest as it takes up the most space from left to right.

   The correct answer is C.

6. Explanation: Choice B is the widest as it takes up the most space from left to right.

   The correct answer is B.

7. Explanation: Choice A is the skinniest as it takes up the least space from left to right.

   The correct answer is A.

8. Explanation: Choice D is the skinniest as it takes up the least space from left to right.

   The correct answer is D.

9. Explanation: Choice C and the arrow are the same length. If you put them up against each other, they occupy the same amount of space from left to right.

   The correct answer is C.

10. Explanation: Choice D and the arrow are the same length. If you put them up against each other, they occupy the same amount of space from left to right.

The correct answer is D.

11. Explanation: Choice A is longer than the arrow. If you put them up against each other, the cloud will occupy more space than the arrow.

The correct answer is A.

12. Explanation: Choice B is shorter than the arrow. If you put them up against each other, the can occupies not as much space as the arrow from left to right.

The correct answer is B.

1. Which object is wider than the arrow?

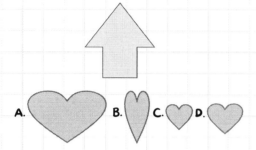

2. Which object is wider than the arrow?

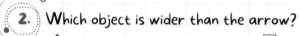

3. Which object is skinnier than the arrow?

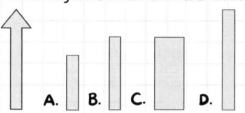

4. Which object is skinnier than the arrow?

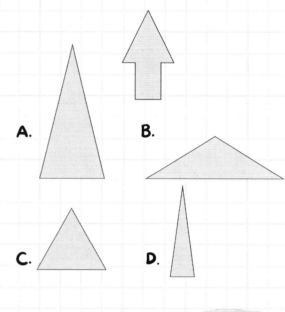

Measure an object using ruler, yardstick, meter stick, measuring tape

5. Which tool would be the best to use to measure the length of a room?

  A. Ruler
  B. Measuring tape
  C. Yardstick
  D. Meter stick

6. What is one thing in your house you could measure using a ruler?

_____

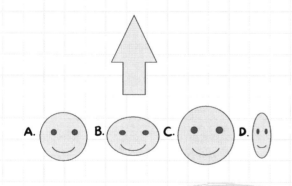

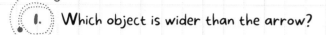

7. What is one thing in your house you could measure using a yardstick? _____

Difficulty: Medium

8. Which tool would be the best to use to measure around a tree trunk?

A. Ruler
B. Meter stick
C. Yardstick
D. Measuring tape

Difficulty: Medium

9. Measure something in your house smaller than a ruler and record the object and the measurement here.

Difficulty: Medium

10. Measure something in your house larger than a ruler and record the object and measurement here.

Difficulty: Medium

11. Measure something in your house larger than a yardstick or meter stick. Record the object and measurement here.

Difficulty: Medium

12. Measure something in your house that is round. Record the object and measurement here.

Difficulty: Medium

13. Measure the line.

A. 6 feet   **C.** 6 m
B. 6 cm   **D.** 6 inches

Difficulty: Medium

14. Measure the line

A. 8 meters   **C.** 8 cm
B. 8 inches   **D.** 8 ft

Difficulty: Medium

15. Measure the line.

A. 3 m
B. B. 3 ft
C. 3 cm
D. 3 inches

Difficulty: Medium

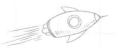

1. Explanation: Choice A is wider than the arrow. If you put them up against each other, choice A occupies more space from left to right.

   The correct answer is A.

2. Explanation: Choice C is wider than the arrow. If you put them up against each other, choice C occupies more space from left to right.

   The correct answer is C.

3. Explanation: : Choice D is skinnier than the arrow. If you put them up against each other, choice D occupies less space from left to right.

   The correct answer is D.

4. Explanation: Choice D is skinnier than the arrow. If you put them up against each other, choice D occupies less space from left to right.

   The correct answer is D.

5. Explanation: To measure a room, the best thing you can use is a measuring tape. If you use a ruler, yardstick, or meter stick, you need to use it multiple times. A measuring tape you can release to get the length you need.

   The correct answer is B.

6. Explanation: Any object that is smaller than the size of a ruler, would be good to measure with a ruler.

   The correct answer should be something in the house less than around 12 inches.

7. Explanation: Any object that is smaller than the size of a yardstick, but larger than the ruler would be good to measure with a yardstick.

   The correct answer should be something in the house large than 12 inches, but smaller than around 36 inches.

8. Explanation: : A measuring tape would be the best to use as it would be able to bend around the tree.

   The correct answer is D.

9. Explanation: Measuring an object smaller than a ruler makes a ruler the best measuring tool to use.

   The correct answer should include the name of the object and the measurement and be less than 12 inches.

10. Explanation: Measuring an object larger than a ruler makes a yardstick, meter stick, or measuring tape the best measuring tool to use.

    The correct answer should include the name of an object and and be larger than 12 inches.

11. Explanation: Measuring an object larger than a yardstick or ruler makes a yardstick, meter stick or measuring tape the best measuring tool to use.

    The correct answer should include the name of an object and be larger than 36 inches..

12. Explanation: Measuring a round object makes a measuring tape the best measuring tool to use.

    The correct answer should include the name of an object and a measurement.

13. Explanation: To measure the line, you put the edge of the ruler on one end of the line and see where the other end of the line shows up in comparison to the ruler. Be sure to pay attention to your units!

    The correct answer is B.

14. Explanation: To measure the line, you put the edge of the ruler on one end of the line and see where the other end of the line shows up in comparison to the ruler. Be sure to pay attention to your units!

    The correct answer is C.

15. Explanation: To measure the line, you put the edge of the ruler on one end of the line and see where the other end of the line shows up in comparison to the ruler. Be sure to pay attention to your units!

    The correct answer is D.

1. Measure the line.

A. 2 inches **B.** 3 inches **C.** 4 inches **D.** 5 inches

2. Measure the line.

A. 2 inches **B.** 3 inches **C.** 4 inches **D.** 5 inches

Difficulty: Medium

3. Measure the line.

A. 2 inches **B.** 3 inches **C.** 4 inches **D.** 5 inches

Difficulty: Medium

4. Measure the line.

A. 2 cm **B.** 3 cm **C.** 4 cm **D.** 5 cm

Difficulty: Medium

5. Measure the line.

A. 2 cm **B.** 3 cm **C.** 4 cm **D.** 5 cm

Difficulty: Medium

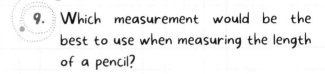

6. Which measurement would be the best to use when measuring a couch?

A. Feet
B. Inches
C. Centimeters
D. Millimeters

Difficulty: Medium

7. Which measurement would be best to use when measuring the height of a bike?

A. Feet
B. Inches
C. Millimeters
D. Meters

Difficulty: Medium

8. Which measurement would be the best to use when measuring the length of a race?

A. Feet
B. Inches
C. Centimeters
D. Meters

Difficulty: Medium

9. Which measurement would be the best to use when measuring the length of a pencil?

A. Feet
B. Miles
C. Centimeters
D. Meters

Difficulty: Medium

10. Which measurement would be the best to use to measure the height of a water bottle?

A. Millimeters
B. Inches
C. Feet
D. Meters

Difficulty: Medium

11. Which measurement would be the best to use to measure the height of a door?

A. Millimeters
B. Inches
C. Feet
D. Meters

Difficulty: Medium

1. Explanation: To measure the line, you put the edge of the ruler on one end of the line and see where the other end of the line shows up in comparison to the ruler. Be sure to pay attention to your units!

   The correct answer is C.

2. Explanation: To measure the line, you put the edge of the ruler on one end of the line and see where the other end of the line shows up in comparison to the ruler. Be sure to pay attention to your units!

   The correct answer is D.

3. Explanation: : To measure the line, you put the edge of the ruler on one end of the line and see where the other end of the line shows up in comparison to the ruler. Be sure to pay attention to your units!

   The correct answer is A.

4. Explanation: To measure the line, you put the edge of the ruler on one end of the line and see where the other end of the line shows up in comparison to the ruler. Be sure to pay attention to your units!

   The correct answer is.B

5. Explanation: To measure the line, you put the edge of the ruler on one end of the line and see where the other end of the line shows up in comparison to the ruler. Be sure to pay attention to your units!

   The correct answer is C.

6. Explanation: To calculate the length of a couch, feet would be the most accurate way to keep track of the length.

   The correct answer is A.

7. Explanation: : To calculate the height of a bike, inches would be the most accurate way to measure the height.

   The correct answer is B.

8. Explanation: To calculate the length of a race, it makes the most sense to use meters, as the other measurements are too small.

   The correct answer is D.

9. Explanation: To calculate the length of a pencil, it makes the most sense to use centimeters as the other measurements are too large.

   The correct answer is C.

10. Explanation: To calculate the height of a water bottle, it makes the most sense to use inches as the other measurements are too large or too small.

    The correct answer is B.

11. Explanation: : To calculate the height of a door, it makes the most sense to use feet as the other measurements are too large or too small.

    The correct answer is C.

1. Which measurement would be the best to measure the length of a sidewalk?

A. Millimeters
B. Inches
C. Feet
D. Meters

Difficulty: Medium

2. Which measurement would be the best to measure the width of a pill?

A. Millimeters
B. Inches
C. Feet
D. Meters

Difficulty: Medium

3. How much longer is line A than line B?

A:
B:

A. 2 cm   **B.** 2 inches   **C.** 4 cm   **D.** 4 inches

Difficulty: Medium

4. How much longer is line A than line B?

A:
B:

A. 1 cm   **B.** 1 in   **C.** 2 in   **D.** 3 in

Difficulty: Medium

5. How much shorter is line A than line B?

A:
B:

A. 5 cm   **B.** 5 in   **C.** 5 ft   **D.** 5 m

Difficulty: Medium

6. How much shorter is line A than line B?

A: ▬▬▬▬
B: ▬▬▬▬▬▬▬▬▬▬▬▬

A. 3 inches   **B.** 3 cm   **C.** 5 inches   **D.** 5 cm

Difficulty: Medium

7. How much longer is line A than line B?

A: ▬▬▬▬▬▬▬▬▬▬▬▬▬▬
B: ▬▬▬▬▬▬

A. 2 inches   **B.** 3 inches   **C.** 3 cm   **D.** 4 inches

Difficulty: Medium

8. How much longer is line A than line B?

A: ▬▬▬▬▬▬▬
B: ▬▬

A. 5 cm   **B.** 4 inches   **C.** 4 cm   **D.** 3 inches

Difficulty: Medium

9. How much shorter is line A than line B?

A: ▬▬▬▬▬▬
B: ▬▬▬▬▬▬▬▬

A. 1 inch   **B.** 2 inches   **C.** 3 inches   **D.** 5 inches

Difficulty: Medium

1. Explanation: To calculate the length of a sidewalk, it makes the most sense to use meters as the other measurements are too small.

   The correct answer is D.

2. Explanation: To calculate the width of a pill, it makes the most sense to use millimeters as the other measurements are too large.

   The correct answer is A.

3. Explanation: To calculate, you measure line A and then measure line B. Then, you subtract the length of line B from the length of line A.

   The correct answer is C.

4. Explanation: To calculate, you measure line A and then measure line B. Then, you subtract the length of line B from the length of line A.

   The correct answer is D.

5. Explanation: To calculate, you measure line A and then measure line B. Then, you subtract the length of line A from the length of line B.

   The correct answer is A.

6. Explanation: To calculate, you measure line A and then measure line B. Then, you subtract the length of line A from the length of line B.

   The correct answer is A.

7. Explanation: To calculate, you measure line A and then measure line B. Then, you subtract the length of line B from the length of line A.

   The correct answer is B.

8. Explanation: To calculate, you measure line A and then measure line B. Then, you subtract the length of line B from the length of line A.

   The correct answer is A.

9. Explanation: To calculate, you measure line A and then measure line B. Then, you subtract the length of line A from the length of line C.

   The correct answer is A.

1. How much shorter is line A than line B?

A:

B:

A. 5 cm   **B.** 5 cm   **C.** 5 inches   **D.** 11 cm

Difficulty: Medium.

2. Measure the line to the nearest $\frac{1}{2}$ inch

A. $2\frac{3}{4}$ inches   **B.** 3 inches   **C.** $3\frac{1}{2}$ in   **D.** $3\frac{1}{4}$ in

Difficulty: Medium

3. Measure the line to the nearest $\frac{1}{2}$ inch

A. $4\frac{3}{4}$ inches   **B.** $5\frac{1}{4}$ inches   **C.** 5 inches   **D.** $5\frac{1}{2}$ inches

Difficulty: Medium

4. Measure the line to the nearest $\frac{1}{4}$ inch

A. 2 inches   **B.** $2\frac{1}{4}$ inches   **C.** $2\frac{1}{2}$ inches   **D.** 3 inches

Difficulty: Medium

5. Measure the line to the nearest $\frac{1}{4}$ inch

A. $3\frac{3}{4}$ inches   **B.** 3 inches   **C.** 4 inches   **D.** $\frac{3}{4}$ inches

Difficulty: Medium

6. Measure the line to the nearest $\frac{1}{2}$ inch

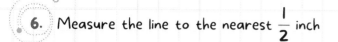

A. $2\frac{1}{2}$ inches   **B.** 3 inches   **C.** $3\frac{1}{2}$ in   **D.** 2 inches

Difficulty: Medium

7. Measure the line to the nearest $\frac{1}{2}$ inch

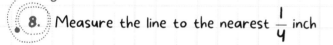

A. 5 inches   **B.** $5\frac{1}{2}$ inches   **C.** 6 in   **D.** $6\frac{1}{2}$ in

Difficulty: Medium

8. Measure the line to the nearest $\frac{1}{4}$ inch

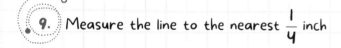

A. $4\frac{3}{4}$ inches   **B.** 3 inches   **C.** $3\frac{3}{4}$ inches   **D.** $\frac{3}{4}$ inches

Difficulty: Medium

9. Measure the line to the nearest $\frac{1}{4}$ inch

A. $1\frac{1}{4}$ inches   **B.** 1 inches   **C.** $1\frac{1}{2}$ inches   **D.** $1\frac{3}{4}$ inches

Difficulty: Medium

10. What number should go in the missing box?

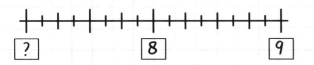

A. 7   C. 9
B. 8   D. 10

Difficulty: Medium

11. What number should go in the missing box?

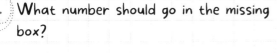

A. 3   C. 5
B. 4   D. 6

Difficulty: Medium

12. What number should go in the missing box?

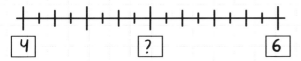

A. 10   C. 12
B. 11   D. 13

Difficulty: Medium

13. What number should go in the missing box?

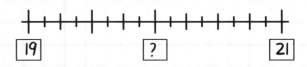

A. 20   C. 22
B. 21   D. 23

Difficulty: Medium

14. What number should go in the missing box?

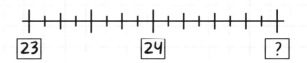

A. 28   C. 26
B. 27   D. 25

Difficulty: Medium

15. What number should go in the missing box?

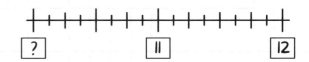

A. 9   C. 11
B. 10   D. 12

Difficulty: Medium

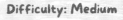

1. Explanation: To calculate, you measure line A and then measure line B. Then, you subtract the length of line A from the length of line C.

   The correct answer is A.

2. Explanation: To measure the line, you put the edge of the ruler on one end of the line and see where the other end of the line shows up in comparison to the ruler. Be sure to pay attention to your units!

   The correct answer is C.

3. Explanation: To measure the line, you put the edge of the ruler on one end of the line and see where the other end of the line shows up in comparison to the ruler. Be sure to pay attention to your units!

   The correct answer is D.

4. Explanation: To measure the line, you put the edge of the ruler on one end of the line and see where the other end of the line shows up in comparison to the ruler. Be sure to pay attention to your units!

   The correct answer is B.

5. Explanation: To measure the line, you put the edge of the ruler on one end of the line and see where the other end of the line shows up in comparison to the ruler. Be sure to pay attention to your units!

   The correct answer is A.

6. Explanation: To measure the line, you put the edge of the ruler on one end of the line and see where the other end of the line shows up in comparison to the ruler. Be sure to pay attention to your units!

   The correct answer is A.

7. Explanation: To measure the line, you put the edge of the ruler on one end of the line and see where the other end of the line shows up in comparison to the ruler. Be sure to pay attention to your units!

   The correct answer is C.

8. Explanation: To measure the line, you put the edge of the ruler on one end of the line and see where the other end of the line shows up in comparison to the ruler. Be sure to pay attention to your units!

   The correct answer is A.

9. Explanation: To measure the line, you put the edge of the ruler on one end of the line and see where the other end of the line shows up in comparison to the ruler. Be sure to pay attention to your units!

   The correct answer is A.

10. Explanation: On this number line, the number missing is before 8. The whole number before 8 is 7.

    The correct answer is A.

11. Explanation: On this number line, the number missing is before 6. The whole number before 6 is 5.

    The correct answer is C.

12. Explanation: On this number line, the number missing is after 10. The whole number after 10 is 11.

    The correct answer is B.

13. Explanation: On this number line, the number missing is after 19. The whole number after 19 is 20.

    The correct answer is A.

14. Explanation: On this number line, the number missing is after 24. The whole number after 24 is 25.

    The correct answer is D.

15. Explanation: On this number line, the number missing is before 11. The whole number before 11 is 10.

    The correct answer is B.

1. What number should go in the missing box?

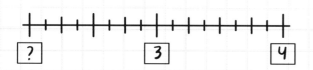

?   **3**   **4**

A. 4   **C.** 2

B. 3   **D.** 1

Difficulty: Medium.

2. What number should go in the missing box?

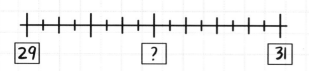

29   **?**   **31**

A. 27   **C.** 29

B. 28   **D.** 30

Difficulty: Medium

3. Which container holds around 1 liter?

A. A drinking straw
B. A gallon container
C. A drinking glass
D. A sand bucket

Difficulty: Hard

4. Which object weighs around 1 gram?

A. A coconut
B. A ponytail holder
C. A teddy bear
D. A textbook

Difficulty: Hard

5. Which amount should be measured in milliliters?

A. The weight of a tadpool
B. A dose of medicine
C. The amount of water you drink in a day
D. The amount of water in a bathtub

Difficulty: Hard

6. Which object weighs around 1 kilogram?

A. An apple
B. A large dog
C. A text book
D. A tree

Difficulty: Hard

7. Which unit should you use to measure the amount of water a bathtub?

   A. Liters
   B. Kilograms
   C. Grams
   D. Gallons

   Difficulty: Hard

8. Which unit should you use to measure the weight of a watermelon?

   A. Liters
   B. Kilograms
   C. Grams
   D. Gallons

   Difficulty: Hard

9. Which unit should you use to measure the amount of water in a sink?

   A. Liters
   B. Kilograms
   C. Grams
   D. Gallons

   Difficulty: Hard

10. Which unit should you use to measure the weight of a playing card?

    A. Liters
    B. Kilograms
    C. Grams
    D. Gallons

    Difficulty: Hard

1. Explanation: On this number line, the number missing is before 3. The whole number before 3 is 2.

   The correct answer is C.

2. Explanation: On this number line, the number missing is after 29. The whole number after 29 is 30.

   The correct answer is D.

3. Explanation: Out of these choices, the item that holds closest to one liter of water is a sand bucket.

   The correct answer is D.

4. Explanation: Out of these choices, the item that weighs closest to a gram is a ponytail holder.

   The correct answer is B.

5. Explanation: Milliliter relates to liquid measurement. The closest liquid that should be measured in milliliters is a dose of medicine.

   The correct answer is B.

6. Explanation: Out of these choices, the item that weighs closest to a kilogram is a textbook.

   The correct answer is C.

7. Explanation: Gallons is the largest unit provided to measure volume.

   The correct answer is D.

8. Explanation: Kilograms is the largest unit provided to measure weight.

   The correct answer is B.

9. Explanation: Liters is the smallest unit provided to measure volume.

   The correct answer is A.

10. Explanation: Grams is the smallest unit provided to measure weight.

    The correct answer is C.

1. How many unit squares make up the area of the rectangle?

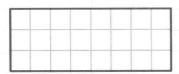

A. 20   C. 24

B. 22   D. 28

Difficulty: Hard

2. How many unit squares make up the area of the rectangle?

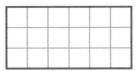

A. 18   C. 22

B. 20   D. 24

Difficulty: Hard

3. How many unit squares make up the area of the rectangle?

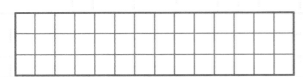

A. 36   C. 40

B. 38   D. 42

Difficulty: Hard

4. How many unit squares make up the area of the rectangle?

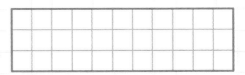

A. 22   C. 44

B. 33   D. 48

Difficulty: Hard

5. How many unit squares make up the area of the rectangle?

A. 22   C. 44

B. 33   D. 48

Difficulty: Hard

6. How many unit squares make up the area of the rectangle?

A. 6   C. 4

B. 10   D. 16

Difficulty: Hard

7. How many unit squares make up the area of the rectangle?

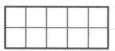

A. 8   C. 12

B. 10   D. 14

8. How many unit squares make up the area of the square?

A. 9   C. 11

B. 10   D. 12

9. If a rectangle has a length of 4 squares and a width of 2 squares, what is the area of the rectangle?

A. 2   C. 6

B. 4   D. 8

10. If a rectangle has a length of 5 squares and a width of 4 squares, what is the area of the rectangle?

A. 10   C. 20

B. 15   D. 25

11. If a rectangle has a length of 8 squares and a width of 1 square, what is the area of the rectangle?

A. 2   C. 8

B. 4   D. 16

12. If a rectangle has a length of 6 squares and a width of 3 squares, what is the area of the rectangle?

A. 18   C. 22

B. 20   D. 24

13. If a rectangle has a length of 2 squares and a width of 3 squares, what is the area of the rectangle?

A. 4   C. 7

B. 5   D. 6

14. If a rectangle has a length of **5** squares and a width of **8** squares, what is the area of the rectangle?

A. 38   **C.** 42

B. 40   **D.** 44

Difficulty: Hard

15. If a rectangle has a length of **7** squares and a width of **2** squares, what is the area of the rectangle?

A. 14   **C.** 16

B. 15   **D.** 17

Difficulty: Hard

16. If a rectangle has a length of **9** squares and a width of **4** squares, what is the area of the rectangle?

A. 28   **C.** 36

B. 32   **D.** 40

Difficulty: Hard

17. How many unit squares make up the area of the rectangle?

A. 8   **C.** 12

B. 10   **D.** 14

Difficulty: Hard

18. How many unit squares make up the area of the rectangle?

A. 8   **C.** 12

B. 10   **D.** 14

Difficulty: Hard

19. How many unit squares make up the area of the rectangle?

A. 10   **C.** 30

B. 20   **D.** 40

Difficulty: Hard

1. Explanation: To find the area using unit squares, you count how many squares make up the larger shape. This rectangle is 8 squares long and 3 squares wide. Therefore the area is 24 unit squares.

   The correct answer is C.

2. Explanation: To find the area using unit squares, you count how many squares make up the larger shape. This rectangle is 6 squares long and 3 squares wide. Therefore the area is 18 unit squares.

   The correct answer is A.

3. Explanation: To find the area using unit squares, you count how many squares make up the larger shape. This rectangle is 14 squares long and 3 squares wide. Therefore the area is 42 unit squares.

   The correct answer is D.

4. Explanation: To find the area using unit squares, you count how many squares make up the larger shape. This rectangle is 11 squares long and 3 squares wide. Therefore the area is 33 unit squares.

   The correct answer is B.

5. Explanation: To find the area using unit squares, you count how many squares make up the larger shape. This rectangle is 11 squares long and 2 squares wide. Therefore the area is 22 unit squares.

   The correct answer is A.

6. Explanation: To find the area using unit squares, you count how many squares make up the larger shape. This rectangle is 8 squares long and 2 squares wide. Therefore the area is 16 unit squares.

   The correct answer is D.

7. Explanation: To find the area using unit squares, you count how many squares make up the larger shape. This rectangle is 5 squares long and 2 squares wide. Therefore the area is 10 unit squares.

   The correct answer is B.

8. Explanation: To find the area using unit squares, you count how many squares make up the larger shape. This square is 3 squares long and 3 squares wide. Therefore the area is 9 unit squares.

   The correct answer is A.

9. Explanation: To calculate the area, you can take the length times the width. A length of 4 times a width of 2 gives you an area of 8.

   The correct answer is D.

10. Explanation: To calculate the area, you can take the length times the width. A length of **5** times a width of **4** gives you an area of **20**.

The correct answer is C.

11. Explanation: To calculate the area, you can take the length times the width. A length of **8** times a width of **I** gives you an area of **8**.

The correct answer is C.

12. Explanation: To calculate the area, you can take the length times the width. A length of **6** times a width of **3** gives you an area of **18**.

The correct answer is A.

13. Explanation: To calculate the area, you can take the length times the width. A length of **2** times a width of **3** gives you an area of **6**.

The correct answer is D.

14. Explanation: To calculate the area, you can take the length times the width. A length of **5** times a width of **8** gives you an area of **40**.

The correct answer is B.

15. Explanation: To calculate the area, you can take the length times the width. A

length of **7** times a width of **2** gives you an area of **14**.

The correct answer is A.

16. Explanation: To calculate the area, you can take the length times the width. A length of **9** times a width of **4** gives you an area of **36**.

The correct answer is C.

17. Explanation: To find the area using unit squares, you count how many squares make up the larger shape. This rectangle is **4** squares long and **2** squares wide. Therefore the area is **8** unit squares.

The correct answer is A.

18. Explanation: To find the area using unit squares, you count how many squares make up the larger shape. This rectangle is **4** squares long and **3** squares wide. Therefore the area is **12** unit squares.

The correct answer is C.

19. Explanation: To find the area using unit squares, you count how many squares make up the larger shape. This rectangle is **5** squares long and **4** squares wide. Therefore the area is **20** unit squares.

The correct answer is B.

1. How many unit squares make up the area of the rectangle?

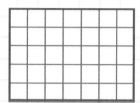

A. 20   **C.** 30

B. 25   **D.** 35

Difficulty: Hard

2. How many unit squares make up the area of the rectangle?

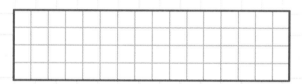

A. 64   **C.** 60

B. 62   **D.** 58

Difficulty: Hard

3. How many unit squares make up the area of the rectangle?

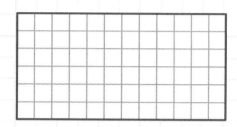

A. 66   **C.** 70

B. 68   **D.** 72

Difficulty: Hard

4. How many unit squares make up the area of the rectangle?

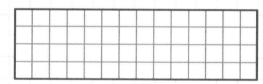

A. 54   **C.** 58

B. 56   **D.** 60

Difficulty: Hard

5. How many unit squares make up the area of the rectangle?

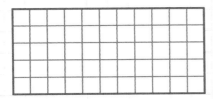

A. 40   C. 55
B. 45   D. 65

Difficulty: Hard

6. If a rectangle has a length of 7 and a width of 6, what is the area of the rectangle?

A. 38   C. 42
B. 40   D. 44

Difficulty: Hard

7. If a rectangle has a length of 8 and a width of 2, what is the area of the rectangle?

A. 16   C. 20
B. 18   D. 22

Difficulty: Hard

8. If a rectangle has a length of 4 and a width of 9, what is the area of the rectangle?

A. 36   C. 32
B. 34   D. 30

Difficulty: Hard

9. If a rectangle has a length of 3 and a width of 5, what is the area of the rectangle?

A. 10   C. 20
B. 15   D. 25

Difficulty: Hard

10. If a rectangle has a length of 10 and a width of 7, what is the area of the rectangle?

A. 60   C. 80
B. 70   D. 90

Difficulty: Hard

11. If a rectangle has a length of 2 and a width of 4, what is the area of the rectangle?

A. 6   C. 10
B. 8   D. 12

Difficulty: Hard

1. If a rectangle has a length of 3 and a width of 8, what is the area of the rectangle?

　A. 22　　　　**C.** 26
　B. 24　　　　**D.** 28

Difficulty: Hard

2. If a rectangle has a length of 5 and a width of 9, what is the area of the rectangle?

　A. 40　　　　**C.** 50
　B. 45　　　　**D.** 55

Difficulty: Hard

3. If the each side of the following shape is 12 inches, what is the perimeter of the polygon?

　A. 24　　　　**C.** 48
　B. 36　　　　**D.** 144

Difficulty: Hard

4. If the each side of the following shape is 8 centimeters, what is the perimeter of the polygon?

　A. 24　　　　**C.** 32
　B. 16　　　　**D.** 8

Difficulty: Hard

5. If the each side of the following shape is 13 feet, what is the perimeter of the polygon?

　A. 26　　　　**C.** 39
　B. 52　　　　**D.** 42

Difficulty: Hard

6. If the each side of the following shape is **7** meters, what is the perimeter of the polygon?

A. 30   C. 40
B. 35   D. 45

Difficulty: Hard

7. If the each side of the following shape is **10** feet, what is the perimeter of the polygon?

A. 50   C. 70
B. 60   D. 80

Difficulty: Hard

8. If the each side of the following shape is **6** centimeters, what is the perimeter of the polygon?

A. 12   C. 24
B. 18   D. 30

Difficulty: Hard

9. If the each side of the following shape is **15** inches, what is the perimeter of the polygon?

A. 45   C. 75
B. 60   D. 90

Difficulty: Hard

10. If the each side of the following shape is **20** yards, what is the perimeter of the polygon?

A. 80   C. 120
B. 100   D. 140

Difficulty: Hard

1. Explanation: To find the area using unit squares, you count how many squares make up the larger shape. This rectangle is 7 squares long and 5 squares wide. Therefore the area is 35 unit squares.

   The correct answer is D.

2. Explanation: To find the area using unit squares, you count how many squares make up the larger shape. This rectangle is 16 squares long and 4 squares wide. Therefore the area is 64 unit squares.

   The correct answer is A.

3. Explanation: To find the area using unit squares, you count how many squares make up the larger shape. This rectangle is 12 squares long and 6 squares wide. Therefore the area is 72 unit squares.

   The correct answer is D.

4. Explanation: To find the area using unit squares, you count how many squares make up the larger shape. This rectangle is 14 squares long and 4 squares wide. Therefore the area is 56 unit squares.

   The correct answer is B.

5. Explanation: To find the area using unit squares, you count how many squares make up the larger shape. This rectangle is 11 squares long and 5 squares wide. Therefore the area is 55 unit squares.

   The correct answer is C.

6. Explanation: To calculate the area, you can take the length times the width. The length is 7 and the width is 6, so the area is 42.

   The correct answer is C.

7. Explanation: To calculate the area, you can take the length times the width. The length is 8 and the width is 2, so the area is 16.

   The correct answer is A.

8. Explanation: To calculate the area, you can take the length times the width. The length is 4 and the width is 9, so the area is 36.

   The correct answer is A.

9. Explanation: To calculate the area, you can take the length times the width. The length is 3 and the width is 5, so the area is 15.

   The correct answer is B.

10. Explanation: To calculate the area, you can take the length times the width.

The length is 10 and the width is 7, so the area is 70.

The correct answer is B.

11. Explanation: To calculate the area, you can take the length times the width. The length is 2 and the width is 4, so the area is 8.

The correct answer is B.

12. Explanation: To calculate the area, you can take the length times the width. The length is 3 and the width is 8, so the area is 24.

The correct answer is B.

13. Explanation: To calculate the area, you can take the length times the width. The length is 5 and the width is 9, so the area is 45.

The correct answer is B.

14. Explanation: To find the perimeter of a rhombus with a side of 12 cm, you add 12 + 12 + 12 + 12.

The correct answer is C.

15. Explanation: To find the perimeter of a triangle with a side of 8 cm, you add 8 + 8 + 8.

The correct answer is A.

16. Explanation: To find the perimeter of a square with a side of 13 feet, you add 13 + 13 + 13 + 13.

The correct answer is B.

17. Explanation: To find the perimeter of a pentagon with a side of 7 meters, you add 7 + 7 + 7 + 7 + 7.

The correct answer is B.

18. Explanation: To find the perimeter of a hexagon with a side of 10 feet, you add 10 + 10 + 10 + 10 + 10 + 10.

The correct answer is B.

19. Explanation: To find the perimeter of a triangle with a side of 6 centimeters, you add 6 + 6 + 6.

The correct answer is B.

20. Explanation: To find the perimeter of a parallelogram with a side of 15 inches, you add 15 + 15 + 15 + 15.

The correct answer is B.

21. Explanation: To find the perimeter of a pentagon with a side of 20 meters, you add 20 + 20 + 20 + 20 + 20.

The correct answer is B.

1. Which clock shows 6:00?

A.

C.

B.

D.

Difficulty: Easy

2. Which clock shows 3:30?

A.

C.

B.

D.

Difficulty: Easy

3. What is the time on the clock?

A. 9:00   C. 6:09
B. 9:30   D. 6:30

Difficulty: Easy

4. What is the time on the clock?

A. 12:00   C. 2:30
B. 2:00   D. 12:30

Difficulty: Easy

5. Draw 4:00 on the clock.

Difficulty: Easy

6. Draw 12:30 on the clock.

Difficulty: Easy

7. Draw **5:30** on the clock.

Difficulty: Easy

8. Draw **7:00** on the clock.

Difficulty: Easy

9. Which clock shows **1:35**?

A.

C.

B.

D.

Difficulty: Medium

10. Which clock shows **10:20**?

A.

C.

B.

D.

Difficulty: Medium

11. What is the time on the clock?

A. 4:55   C. 11:05

B. 5:55   D. 5:11

Difficulty: Medium

12. What is the time on the clock?

A. 5:01   C. 1:10

B. 1:25   D. 5:05

Difficulty: Medium

1. Explanation: To tell time, the small hand points to the hour and the large hand points to the minute. To show **6:00**, the small hand should point to the **6** and the large hand should point to the 12.

   The correct answer is A.

2. Explanation: To tell time, the small hand points to the hour and the large hand points to the minute. To show **3:30**, the small hand should point to the **3** and the large hand should point to the 6.

   The correct answer is C.

3. Explanation: To tell time, the small hand points to the hour and the large hand points to the minute. The small hand is pointing to the **9** and the large hand is pointing to the **6**, so the time is 9:30.

   The correct answer is B.

4. Explanation: To tell time, the small hand points to the hour and the large hand points to the minute. The small hand is pointing to the **2** and the large hand is pointing to the **12**, so the time is **2:00**.

   The correct answer is B.

5. Explanation: To tell time, the small hand points to the hour and the large hand points to the minute. The small hand is pointing to the **4** and the large hand is pointing to the **12**, so the time is **4:00**.

   Correct answer: Students should draw a minute hand pointing to the 12 and an hour hand pointing to the 4.

6. Explanation: To tell time, the small hand points to the hour and the large hand points to the minute. The small hand is pointing to the **12** and the large hand is pointing to the **6**, so the time is **12:30**.

   Correct answer: Students should draw a minute hand pointing to the 6 and an hour hand pointing to the 12.

7. Explanation: To tell time, the small hand points to the hour and the large hand points to the minute. The small hand is pointing to the **5** and the large hand is pointing to the **6**, so the time is **5:30**.

Correct answer: Students should draw a minute hand pointing to the 6 and an hour hand pointing to the 5.

8. Explanation: To tell time, the small hand points to the hour and the large hand points to the minute. The small hand is pointing to the **7** and the large hand is pointing to the **12**, so the time is **7:00**.

Correct answer: Students should draw a minute hand pointing to the 12 and an hour hand pointing to the 7.

9. Explanation: To tell time, the small hand points to the hour and the large hand points to the minute. To show **1:35**, the small hand should point to the **1** and the large hand should point to the **7**.

The correct answer is C.

10. Explanation: To tell time, the small hand points to the hour and the large hand points to the minute. To show **10:20**, the small hand should point to the **10** and the large hand should point to the **4**.

The correct answer is A.

11. Explanation: To tell time, the small hand points to the hour and the large hand points to the minute. The small hand is pointing to the **5** and the large hand is pointing to the **11**, so the time is **4:55**.

The correct answer is A.

12. Explanation: To tell time, the small hand points to the hour and the large hand points to the minute. The small hand is pointing to the **5** and the large hand is pointing to the **1**, so the time is **5:05**.

The correct answer is D.

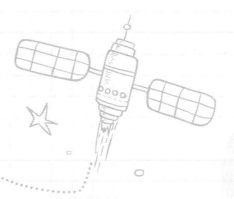

1. Draw 1:45 on the clock.

Difficulty: Medium

2. Draw 7:10 on the clock.

Difficulty: Medium

3. Draw 8:40 on the clock.

Difficulty: Medium

4. Draw 11:50 on the clock.

Difficulty: Medium

5. Which clock shows 4:57?

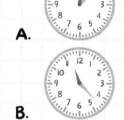

A.   C.

B.   D.

Difficulty: Hard

6. Which clock shows 8:14?

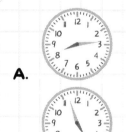

A.   C.

B.   D.

Difficulty: Hard

7. What is the time on the clock?

A. 11:21   **C.** 4:57
B. 4:11   **D.** 11:04

Difficulty: Hard

8. What is the time on the clock?

A. 3:40   **C.** 2: 06
B. 2:33   **D.** 6:12

Difficulty: Hard

9. Draw 1:48 on the clock.

Difficulty: Hard

10. Draw 3:29 on the clock.

Difficulty: Hard

11. Draw 5:38 on the clock.

Difficulty: Hard

12. Draw 7:22 on the clock.

Difficulty: Hard

1. Explanation: To tell time, the small hand points to the hour and the large hand points to the minute. The small hand is pointing to the 1 and the large hand is pointing to the 9, so the time is 1:45.

   Correct answer: Students should draw a minute hand pointing to the 9 and an hour hand pointing to the 1.

2. Explanation: To tell time, the small hand points to the hour and the large hand points to the minute. The small hand is pointing to the 7 and the large hand is pointing to the 2, so the time is 7:10.

   Correct answer: Students should draw a minute hand pointing to the 2 and an hour hand pointing to the 7.

3. Explanation: To tell time, the small hand points to the hour and the large hand points to the minute. The small hand is pointing to the 8 and the large hand is pointing to the 8, so the time is 8:40.

   Correct answer: Students should draw a minute hand pointing to the 8 and an hour hand pointing to the 8.

4. Explanation: To tell time, the small hand points to the hour and the large hand points to the minute. The small hand is pointing to the 11 and the large hand is pointing to the 10, so the time is 11:50.

   Correct answer: Students should draw a minute hand pointing to the 10 and an hour hand pointing to the 11.

5. Explanation: To tell time, the small hand points to the hour and the large hand points to the minute. To show 4:57, the small hand should point to the 4 and the large hand should point two marks after the 11.

   The correct answer is C.

6. Explanation: To tell time, the small hand points to the hour and the large hand points to the minute. To show 8:14, the small hand should point to the 8 and the large hand should point four marks after the 2.

   The correct answer is A.

7. Explanation: To tell time, the small hand points to the hour and the large hand points to the minute. The small hand is pointing to the 11 and the large hand is pointing one mark after the 4, so the time is 11:21.

   The correct answer is A.

8. Explanation: To tell time, the small hand points to the hour and the large hand points to the minute. The small hand is pointing to the 2 and the large hand is pointing three marks after the 6, so the time is 2:33.

   The correct answer is B.

9. Explanation: To tell time, the small hand points to the hour and the large hand points to the minute. The small hand is pointing to the 1 and the large hand is slightly past the 9, showing the time of 1:48.

   Correct answer: Students should draw a minute hand three marks past the 9 and an hour hand pointing to the 1.

10. Explanation: To tell time, the small hand points to the hour and the large hand points to the minute. The small hand is pointing to the 3 and the large hand is slightly past the 5, showing the time of 3:29.

    Correct answer: Students should draw a minute hand four marks past the 5 and an hour hand pointing to the 3.

11. Explanation: To tell time, the small hand points to the hour and the large hand points to the minute. The small hand is pointing to the 5 and the large hand is slightly past the 7, showing the time of 5:38.

    Correct answer: Students should draw a minute hand two marks past the 7 and an hour hand pointing to the 5.

12. Explanation: To tell time, the small hand points to the hour and the large hand points to the minute. The small hand is pointing to the 7 and the large hand is slightly past the 4, showing the time of 7:22.

    Correct answer: Students should draw a minute hand two marks past the 4 and an hour hand pointing to the 7.

☀ Measurement and Data ☀
☀ Measurement of Data ☀

Use the below graph to answer the questions 1-3.

School Transportation

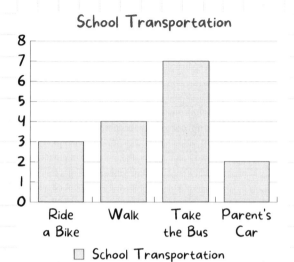

☐ School Transportation

1. How many total people were surveyed?

A. 3   C. 14
B. 7   D. 16

Difficulty: Easy

2. How many people ride a bike to school?

A. 2   C. 3
B. 7   D. 4

Difficulty: Easy

3. How many more people walk than ride in a car?

A. 2   C. 4
B. 3   D. 5

Difficulty: Easy

Use the following line plot to answer questions 4-6.

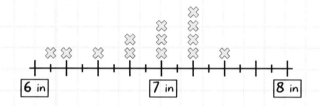

4. What is the length of the longest pencil in the class?

A. $7\frac{1}{4}$ in   C. $7\frac{1}{2}$ in
B. 7 in   D. $6\frac{1}{8}$ in

Difficulty: Medium

5. What is the length of the shortest pencil in the class?

A. $7\frac{1}{4}$ in   C. $7\frac{1}{2}$ in
B. 7 in   D. $6\frac{1}{8}$ in

Difficulty: Medium

6. What pencil length occurs most often in the class?

A. $7\frac{1}{4}$ in   C. $7\frac{1}{2}$ in

B. 7 in   D. $6\frac{1}{8}$ in

Difficulty: Medium

Use the following graph to answer questions 7-9.

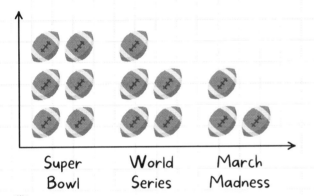

Super Bowl   World Series   March Madness

7. How many people were surveyed?

A. 6   C. 5

B. 14   D. 3

Difficulty: Medium

8. How many people like to watch the Super Bowl?

A. 6   C. 5

B. 14   D. 3

Difficulty: Medium

9. How many more people like to watch the World Series than March Madness?

A. 0   C. 2

B. 1   D. 3

Difficulty: Medium

Use the bar graph to answer questions 10-12.

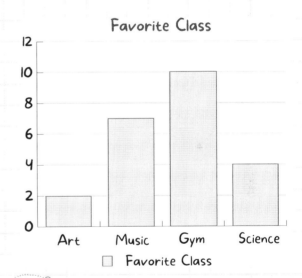

Favorite Class

☐ Favorite Class

10. How many total students were surveyed?

A. 23   C. 26

B. 22   D. 25

Difficulty: Medium

11. How many more people prefer music to art?

A. 2   C. 4

B. 3   D. 5

Difficulty: Medium

12. What was the most popular choice for students?

A. Science   C. Music

B. Gym   D. Art

Difficulty: Medium

13. If the scale of a picture graph says 1 book = 4 students and the category has 5 books, how many students voted for that choice?

A. 15   C. 25

B. 20   D. 30

Difficulty: Medium

14. If the scale of a bar graph says 1 pie = 2 students and the category has 3 pies, how many students voted for that choice?

A. 2   C. 6

B. 4   D. 8

Difficulty: Medium

15. If the scale of a bar graph says 1 sun = 4 students and the category has $2\frac{1}{2}$ suns, how many students voted for that choice?

A. 10   C. 6

B. 8   D. 4

Difficulty: Medium

16. If the scale of a bar graph says 1 leaf = 3 students and the category has 5 leaves, how many students voted for that choice?

A. 15   C. 8

B. 12   D. 4

Difficulty: Medium

17. If the scale of a bar graph says 1 face = 8 students and the category has $4\frac{1}{2}$ faces, how many students voted for that choice?

A. 30   C. 34

B. 32   D. 36

Difficulty: Medium

1. Explanation: To find the total number of people surveyed, you should take 3+4+7+2.

   The correct answer is D.

2. Explanation: To find how many people ride a bike, you need to count how many people are in that column on the graph.

   The correct answer is C.

3. Explanation: To answer, you need to take the number of people who walk minus the number of people who ride in a car. 4 - 2 = 2

   The correct answer is A.

4. Explanation: The longest pencil in the class is marked on the $7\frac{1}{2}$ line of the line plot.

   The correct answer is C.

5. Explanation: The shortest pencil in the class is marked on the $6\frac{1}{8}$ line of the line plot.

   The correct answer is D.

6. Explanation: There are four people who have pencils that are $7\frac{1}{4}$ inches long. that is the most out of any category.

   The correct answer is A.

7. Explanation: To find out how many people were surveyed, you need to count how many total balls there are in each category. 6 + 5 + 3 = 14

   The correct answer is B.

8. Explanation: To find out how many people like to watch the Super Bowl, you need to count how many balls are in that category alone.

   The correct answer is A.

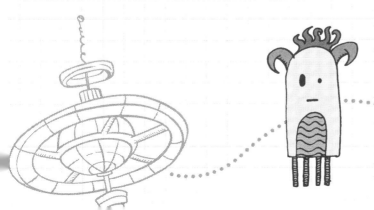

9. Explanation: To find out how many more people watch the World Series than March Madness, you need to compare the two categories. 5 - 3 = 2

    The correct answer is C.

10. Explanation: To find the total students, you have to add them together. Be careful! The scale is every 2 students is a line, not every 1 student.

    The correct answer is A.

11. Explanation: To find the answer you need to take the number of students who prefer music and subtract the number of students who prefer art. 7 - 2 = 5

    The correct answer is D.

12. Explanation: The most popular choice has the most amount of votes. In this graph, gym has the most votes with 10.

    The correct answer is B.

13. Explanation: If 1 book is 4 students, then 5 books is 4 x 5 or 20 students.

    The correct answer is B.

14. Explanation: If 1 pie is 2 students, then 3 pies is 2 x 3 or 6 students.

    The correct answer is C.

15. Explanation: If 1 sun is 4 students, then 2 suns is 8 students. $\frac{1}{2}$ sun is 2 students. 8 + 2 = 10

    The correct answer is A.

16. Explanation: If 1 leaf is 3 students, then 5 leaves is 15 students.

    The correct answer is A.

17. Explanation: If 1 face is 8 students, then 4 faces is 32 students. $\frac{1}{2}$ face is 4 students. 32 + 4 = 36

    The correct answer is D.

1. Eli is **63** inches. Sean is **56** inches. How much taller is Eli than Shawn?

A. 7 inches   C. 6 inches
B. 119 inches   D. 114 inches

Difficulty: Medium

2. We received **24** inches of snow last year and **16** inches of snow this year. How many inches of snow did we receive over the last two years?

A. 6 inches   C. 8 inches
B. 30 inches   D. 40 inches

Difficulty: Medium

3. A puppy measures **21** inches after it comes home. If he was **8** inches when he was born, how much has he grown since birth?

A. 9 inches   C. 13 inches
B. 11 inches   D. 15 inches

Difficulty: Medium

4. One snake is **15** inches and another snake is **8** inches. How much longer is the big snake?

A. 4 inches   C. 6 inches
B. 5 inches   D. 7 inches

Difficulty: Medium

5. One tree in our yard is **34** feet high. If we place a swing **20** feet above the ground, how much higher is the tree than the swing?

A. 12 feet   C. 16 feet
B. 14 feet   D. 18 feet

Difficulty: Medium

6. A sunflower in our garden grew **36** inches in 2 months. If it grew another **18** inches in the next month, how higher did it get after 3 months?

A. 46 inches   C. 54 inches
B. 50 inches   D. 58 inches

Difficulty: Medium

7. A suitcase's contents have a weight of 15 kilograms. If we divide the contents into three smaller suitcases, how much does the contents of each suitcase weigh?

A. 10 kg
C. 30 kg
B. 5 kg
D. 45 kg

Difficulty: Hard

8. To make punch, Evie combines 2 liters of fruit punch for every 1 liter of soda. If she has 4 liters of soda, how many liters of fruit punch should she add?

A. 8 liters
C. 2 liters
B. 4 liters
D. 1 liter

Difficulty: Hard

9. Morgan drinks the recommended 2 liters of water a day for a week. How much water has he drunk after 5 days?

A. 10 liters
C. 7 liters
B. 8 liters
D. 5 liters

Difficulty: Hard

10. Miles makes lemonade using 3 liters of water and 1 liter of concentrated lemonade mix. If he is going to make 4 batches, how many total liters will he have?

A. 8 liters
C. 16 liters
B. 12 liters
D. 20 liters

Difficulty: Hard

11. If a pencil weighs 10 grams and you have 18 pencils, what is the total weight?

A. 80 grams
C. 140 grams
B. 100 grams
D. 180 grams

Difficulty: Hard

12. Ryan has 14 dimes and 6 nickels hidden in his sock drawer. How much is his change worth?

A. $1.40
C. $0.30
B. $1.70
D. $0.70

Difficulty: Medium

13. A candy bar costs **$0.82**. Mark has **3** quarters. Does he have enough money to buy a candy bar? Justify your answer.

Difficulty: Medium

14. Tracy goes to a penny candy store. She has **40** pennies or her mom offers her **9** nickels. Should she keep her pennies or trade them for the nickels? Justify your answer.

Difficulty: Medium

15. A book costs **$8**. If Evie wants to buy a copy for herself and her two friends, how much money does she need?

A. $24   C. $20

B. $16   D. $28

Difficulty: Medium

16. Cora's grandparents give her a quarter for every month she has been alive on her birthday. If she is **4**, how much money will she receive from her grandparents?

A. $10   C. $14

B. $12   D. $16

Difficulty: Medium

17. Travis's mom spent a lot of time cleaning out their car. She found **6** quarters, **12** dimes, **5** nickels, and **11** pennies. How much change was in their car?

A. $1.92   C. $3.18

B. $3.06   D. $3.44

Difficulty: Medium

18. Laura begins practicing her piano at **4:45**. If she plays for **35** minutes, what time does she finish?

A. 5:20   C. 5:25

B. 5:15   D. 5:05

Difficulty: Hard

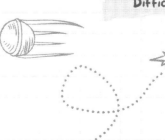

1. Explanation: To find how much taller Eli is, you have to subtract Sean's height from Eli's: **63 - 56.**

   The correct answer is A.

2. Explanation: To calculate the total amount of snow, you have to add the two years together: **24 + 16.**

   The correct answer is D.

3. Explanation: To calculate how much the puppy has grown, you have to subtract its original weight from its current weight: **21 - 8.**

   The correct answer is C.

4. Explanation: To find how much longer the large snake is than the small snake, you should take **15 - 8,** which is **7.**

   The correct answer is D.

5. Explanation: To find how much higher the tree is, you should take **34 - 20,** which is **14.**

   The correct answer is B.

6. Explanation: To find out how high the flower grew, add **36 + 18,** which equals **54.**

   The correct answer is C.

7. Explanation: To divide the weight, you have to take **15** divided by **3** and you get **5 kg** each.

   The correct answer is B.

8. Explanation: To calculate how much punch, you have to take **2 x 4** since **4** is **1 x 4.**

   The correct answer is A.

9. Explanation: To calculate how much water, you have to take **2 liters x 5** days.

   The correct answer is A.

10. Explanation: To calculate his total liters, you take **3 + 1,** and then multiply it by **4,** the number of batches.

    The correct answer is C.

11. Explanation: To calculate the total weight of the pencils, you need to multiply 10x18.

The correct answer is D.

12. Explanation: Each dime is 10 cents and each nickel is 5 cents. 14 dimes is $1.40 and 6 nickels is $0.30.

The correct answer is B.

13. Explanation: Three quarters equals $0.75, so if Mark only has 3 quarters, he does not have enough money to buy a candy bar.

The correct answer is no. Students should mention the total cost of three quarters.

14. Explanation: 9 nickels is worth more than 40 pennies as 9 nickels is $0.45 while 40 pennies is $0.40.

The correct answer is she should take the nickels. Students should mention the total amounts of both coins.

15. Explanation: To calculate, you need to add a book for Evie and two for her friends: 8 + 8 + 8.

The correct answer is A.

16. Explanation: First, you can figure how many quarters she gets a year. If she gets 12 quarters, that will be $3 a year. If she is celebrating 4 years, she will get 3 x 4 = 12.

The correct answer is B.

17. Explanation: You need to calculate how much each amount of change is. First, you take 6 quarters, which is $1.50. Then, 12 dimes is $1.20. Next, 5 nickels is $0.25 and then 11 pennies is $0.11. Finally, you add all those amounts together.

The correct answer is B.

18. Explanation: To calculate 35 minutes past 4:45, you have to count on by 5s. When you get to 5:00, you still have 20 minutes left to practice.

The correct answer is A.

1. Chris leaves school at 2:32. If he arrives home at 2:51, how long does it take him to walk home?

A. 19 minutes
B. 19 hours
C. 9 minutes
D. 10 hours

Difficulty: Hard

2. It will take John 46 minutes to prepare dinner. If he wants to be ready to eat at 6:00, what time should he start to prepare the meal?

A. 6:14
B. 6:46
C. 5:14
D. 5:24

Difficulty: Hard

3. Jack watches 3 shows. Each show is $\frac{1}{2}$ hour. If he starts watching at 3:15, what time will he be done?

A. 5:15
B. 5:00
C. 4:15
D. 4:45

Difficulty: Hard

4. Sam works on his math problems every night. He spends 25 minutes working on his problems. If he works for 4 nights a week, how long does he practice?

A. 1 hour 30 mins
B. 1 hour 40 mins
C. 1 hour 50 mins
D. 2 hours

Difficulty: Hard

5. Matthew has to be at school by 8:05. If it takes him 22 minutes to get to school, what time should he leave his house?

A. 7:47
B. 7:22
C. 8:22
D. 7:43

Difficulty: Hard

6. A rectangle has an area of 21 cm². If the rectangle has a length of 7 cm, what is the width?

A. 4 cm
B. 5 cm
C. 2 cm
D. 3 cm

Difficulty: Hard

7. A rectangle has an area of **64** cm². If the rectangle has a width of **8** cm, what is the length?

A. 6 cm   **C.** 10 cm

B. 8 cm   **D.** 12 cm

Difficulty: Hard

8. Our garden has a length of **10** meters and a width of **6** meters. How much space in our yard does our garden occupy?

A. 60 m².   **C.** 40 m²

B. 50 m²   **D.** 32 m²

Difficulty: Hard

9. We need **80** meters of fence to enclose our rectangular garden. If it has a length of **15** meters, what is the width of the garden?

A. 35   **C.** 25

B. 30   **D.** 20

Difficulty: Hard

10. Our rectangular garden has a width of **12** meters and a length of **14** meters. How much fence would we need to surround the whole garden?

A. 52 m   **C.** 52 cm

B. 52 m²   **D.** 52 ft

Difficulty: Hard

11. The school is designing a new play yard that needs a fence. It will be shaped into a pentagon and the total amount of fence available is **75** meters. How long would each side of the play yard be?

A. 15 meters   **C.** 25 meters

B. 20 meters   **D.** 30 meters

Difficulty: Hard

221

1. Explanation: If he leaves and arrives during the same hour, it takes him less than an hour to walk home. To calculate exactly how many minutes, you should take 51 - 32, for an answer of 19.

   The correct answer is A.

2. Explanation: To solve, you should work backwards from 6:00. 40 minutes before 6:00, would be 5:20 and then 6 minutes before 5:20 would be 5:14.

   The correct answer is C.

3. Explanation: First, you should take 3x 30 minutes, which is 90 minutes. Next you add 90 minutes to 3:15. One hour to 3:15 is 4:15, then another 30 minutes is 4:45.

   The correct answer is D.

4. Explanation: To solve this problem, you should multiply 25 x 4, which is 100 minutes. Then you subtract 1 hour, or 60 minutes, which leaves 40 minutes.

   The correct answer is B.

5. Explanation: To figure this out, you subtract 22 minutes from 8:05. The easiest way to do this, is to reduce 8:05 to 8:00, and 22 minutes to 17 minutes. Then you figure 17 minutes before 8:00, which is 7:43.

   The correct answer is D.

6. Explanation: Area is calculated by length times width. If we are given the area and the length, we can find the width by dividing the area by the length: 21 ÷ 7 = 3

   The correct answer is D.

7. Explanation: Area is calculated by length times width. If we are given the area and the width, we can find the length by dividing the area by the width: **64 ÷ 8 = 8**

   The correct answer is B.

8. Explanation: Area is calculated by length times width. **10 x 6 = 60**

   The correct answer is A.

9. Explanation: Perimeter is calculated by length + length + width + width. If our garden has a length of **15**, we know that the perimeter = width + width + **30**. The perimeter is **80**, so we can determine that the two widths = **50**. That makes 1 width equal to **25**.

   The correct answer is C.

10. Explanation: Perimeter is calculated by width + width + length + length: **12 + 12 + 14 + 14 = 52**. Remember to pay attention to your unit labels!

    The correct answer is A.

11. Explanation: To solve this problem, you should divide **75 ÷ 5**, which equals **15** meters.

    The correct answer is A.

Geometry

1. Attributes of Shapes page

2. 2D Shapes page

3. 3D Shapes page

BRAIN
HUNTER

1. Which attribute defines a rectangle?

A. Size   **C.** Color

B. 4 corners   **D.** 2 Sides

Difficulty: Easy

2. Which attribute defines a circle?

A. 2 sides   **C.** No corners

B. 1 corner   **D.** 4 corners

Difficulty: Easy

3. Which attribute defines a triangle?

A. 3 sides   **C.** 2 sides

B. Large   **D.** blue

Difficulty: Easy

4. Which attribute defines a square?

A. 2 equal sides

B. 4 equal sides

C. 2 corners

D. Small

Difficulty: Easy

5. Which attribute about a square can change?

A. Number of corners

B. Number of sides

C. Its shape

D. Its color

Difficulty: Easy

6. Which attribute about a rectangle can change?

A. 4 corners

B. 4 sides

C. Its size

D. 2 sets of equal sides

Difficulty: Easy

7. Which attribute about a circle can change?

A. It can remove a side.

B. It can add a side.

C. It can get bigger.

D. It can add a corner.

Difficulty: Easy

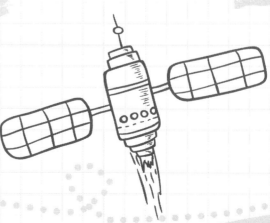

8. Which shape can have different size corners?

A. Triangle   **C.** Square

B. Rectangle   **D.** Circle

Difficulty: Easy

9. Which attribute about a triangle can change?

A. It can remove a side.
B. It can add a side.
C. It can remove a corner.
D. It can become smaller.

Difficulty: Easy

10. Which shape is a triangle?

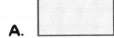

A.   **C.**

B.   **D.**

Difficulty: Easy

11. Which shape is a circle?

A.   **C.**

B. 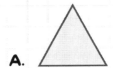   **D.**

Difficulty: Easy

12. Which shape is a rectangle?

A.   **C.**

B.   **D.**

Difficulty: Easy

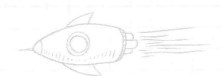

227

1. Explanation: An attribute is a feature that describes a shape. Attributes can be things that define shapes or do not define shapes. Things that define a shape can be attributes such as the number of sides or the number of corners. Things that do not define a shape can be attributes such as color or size. A rectangle is defined as a shape that has 4 corners. Rectangles do not have 2 sides. Rectangles can be a variety of sizes and colors.

   The correct answer is B.

2. Explanation: An attribute is a feature that describes a shape. Attributes can be things that define shapes or do not define shapes. Things that define a shape can be attributes such as the number of sides or the number of corners. Things that do not define a shape can be attributes such as color or size. A circle does not have any sides or corners.

   The correct answer is C.

3. Explanation: An attribute is a feature that describes a shape. Attributes can be things that define shapes or do not define shapes. Things that define a shape can be attributes such as the number of sides or the number of corners. Things that do not define a shape can be attributes such as color or size. A triangle can be any color or size but all triangles have 3 sides.

   The correct answer is A.

4. Explanation: An attribute is a feature that describes a shape. Attributes can be things that define shapes or do not define shapes. Things that define a shape can be attributes such as the number of sides or the number of corners. Things that do not define a shape can be attributes such as color or size. A square can be any size but all squares have 4 equal sides and 4 corners.

   The correct answer is B.

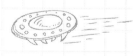

5. Explanation: An attribute is a feature that describes a shape. Attributes can be things that define shapes or do not define shapes. Things that define a shape can be attributes such as the number of sides or the number of corners. Things that do not define a shape can be attributes such as color or size. A square will always keep the same shape with 4 sides and 4 corners but its color can change. The correct answer is D.

    The correct answer is D.

6. Explanation: An attribute is a feature that describes a shape. Attributes can be things that define shapes or do not define shapes. Things that define a shape can be attributes such as the number of sides or the number of corners. Things that do not define a shape can be attributes such as color or size. A rectangle will always have 2 sets of equal sides and 4 corners but its size can change.

    The correct answer is C.

7. Explanation: An attribute is a feature that describes a shape. Attributes can be things that define shapes or do not define shapes. Things that define a shape can be attributes such as the number of sides or the number of corners. Things that do not define a shape can be attributes such as color or size. A circle does not have any sides or corners but it can become bigger or smaller and still be a circle.

    The correct answer is C.

8. Explanation: An attribute is a feature that describes a shape. Attributes can be things that define shapes or do not define shapes. Things that define a shape can be attributes such as the number of sides or the number of corners. Things that do not define a shape can be attributes such as color or size. A triangle can have different size corners but the corners of a rectangle and square do not change. Circles do not have corners.

    The correct answer is A.

9. Explanation: An attribute is a feature that describes a shape. Attributes can be things that define shapes or do not define shapes. Things that define a shape can be attributes such as the number of sides or the number of corners. Things that do not define a shape can be attributes such as color or size. A triangle will always have 3 sides and 3 corners but it can be smaller or larger.

The correct answer is D.

10. Explanation: An attribute is a feature that describes a shape. Attributes can be things that define shapes or do not define shapes. Things that define a shape can be attributes such as the number of sides or the number of corners. Things that do not define a shape can be attributes such as color or size. While all these shapes are roughly the same size and the same color, the only shape that has 3 corners and 3 sides is B so that is the shape that is a triangle.

The correct answer is B.

11. Explanation: An attribute is a feature that describes a shape. Attributes can be things that define shapes or do not define shapes. Things that define a shape can be attributes such as the number of sides or the number of corners. Things that do not define a shape can be attributes such as color or size. While all these shapes are roughly the same size and the same color, the only shape that does not have any corners or sides is shape B so that is the shape that is a circle.

The correct answer is B.

12. Explanation: An attribute is a feature that describes a shape. Attributes can be things that define shapes or do not define shapes. Things that define a shape can be attributes such as the number of sides or the number of corners. Things that do not define a shape can be attributes such as color or size. While all these shapes are roughly the same size and the same color, the only shape that has 4 sides and 4 corners, with two sets of equal sides is shape D, so that is the shape that is a rectangle.

The correct answer is D.

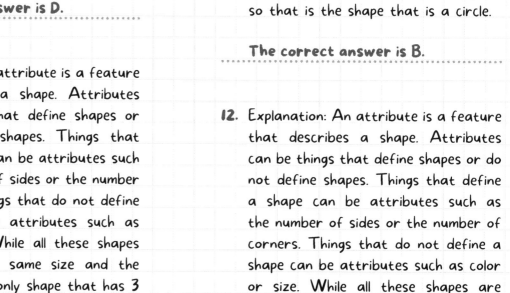

1. Which shape is a square?

A.

C.

B.

D.

Difficulty: Easy

2. Which shape is not a circle?

A.

C.

B.

D.

Difficulty: Easy

3. Which shape is not a rectangle?

A.

C.

B.

D.

Difficulty: Easy

4. Which shape is not a triangle?

A.

C.

B.

D.

Difficulty: Easy

5. Which shape is not a square?

A.

C.

B.

D.

Difficulty: Easy

6. What shape is this and how do you know?

Difficulty: Easy

7. If you draw a shape with no corners, which shape do you draw?

A. Square   **C.** Circle
B. Rectangle   **D.** Triangle

Difficulty: Easy

8. If you draw a shape with three sides, which shape do you draw?

A. Triangle   **C.** Square
B. Circle   **D.** Rectangle

Difficulty: Easy

9. If you draw a shape with four equal sides, which shape do you draw?

A. Rectangle   **C.** Circle
B. Square   **D.** Triangle

Difficulty: Easy

10. If you draw a shape "with **2** different sets of equal sides, which shape do you draw?

A. Triangle   **C.** Square
B. Circle   **D.** Rectangle

Difficulty: Easy

11. Draw a circle.

Difficulty: Easy

12. Draw a square.

Difficulty: Easy

13. Draw a rectangle.

Difficulty: Easy

1. Explanation: An attribute is a feature that describes a shape. Attributes can be things that define shapes or do not define shapes. Things that define a shape can be attributes such as the number of sides or the number of corners. Things that do not define a shape can be attributes such as color or size. While all these shapes are roughly the same size and the same color, the only shape that has 4 equal sides and 4 corners is shape C, so that is the shape that is a square.

   The correct answer is C.

2. Explanation: An attribute is a feature that describes a shape. Attributes can be things that define shapes or do not define shapes. Things that define a shape can be attributes such as the number of sides or the number of corners. Things that do not define a shape can be attributes such as color or size. Shapes B, C, and D all have no corners or sides so they are all circles even though they are different sizes. Shape A is a triangle because it has 3 sides and 3 corners.

   The correct answer is A.

3. Explanation: An attribute is a feature that describes a shape. Attributes can be things that define shapes or do not define shapes. Things that define a shape can be attributes such as the number of sides or the number of corners. Things that do not define a shape can be attributes such as color or size. Shapes A, C, and D all have 4 corners and 4 sides, with 2 equal sets so they are all rectangles even though they are different sizes. Shape B is a circle because it has no sides or corners.

   The correct answer is B.

4. Explanation: An attribute is a feature that describes a shape. Attributes can be things that define shapes or do not define shapes. Things that define a shape can be attributes such as the number of sides or the number of corners. Things that do not define a shape can be attributes such as color or size. Shapes A, B, and D have 3 sides and 3 corners although they are different sizes. Shape C has 4 equal sides and 4 corners so it is a square.

   The correct answer is C.

5. Explanation: An attribute is a feature that describes a shape. Attributes can be things that define shapes or do not define shapes. Things that define a shape can be attributes such as the number of sides or the number of corners. Things that do not define a shape can be attributes such as color or size. Shapes B, C, and D all have 4 corners and 4 equal sides so they are squares. Shape A is a rectangle because it has 2 sets of equal sides and 4 corners.

The correct answer is A.

6. Explanation: An attribute is a feature that describes a shape. Attributes can be things that define shapes or do not define shapes. Things that define a shape can be attributes such as the number of sides or the number of corners. Things that do not define a shape can be attributes such as color or size. This shape is a circle because it has no corners or no sides. It does not matter what its size or color is.

The correct answer is a circle.

7. Explanation: You can use attributes to draw shapes. A circle should be drawn with no corners or sides. A triangle should be drawn with three sides and three corners. A rectangle should be drawn with four corners and two sets of equal sides. A square should be drawn with four corners and four equal sides.

The correct answer is C.

8. Explanation: You can use attributes to draw shapes. A circle should be drawn with no corners or sides. A triangle should be drawn with three sides and three corners. A rectangle should be drawn with four corners and two sets of equal sides. A square should be drawn with four corners and four equal sides.

The correct answer is A.

9. Explanation: You can use attributes to draw shapes. A circle should be drawn with no corners or sides. A triangle should be drawn with three sides and three corners. A rectangle should be drawn with four corners and two sets of equal sides. A square should be drawn with four corners and four equal sides.

The correct answer is B.

10. Explanation: You can use attributes to draw shapes. A circle should be drawn with no corners or sides. A triangle should be drawn with three sides and three corners. A rectangle should be drawn with four corners and two sets of equal sides. A square should be drawn with four corners and four equal sides.

The correct answer is D.

11. Explanation: You can use attributes to draw shapes. A circle should be drawn with no corners or sides. A triangle should be drawn with three sides and three corners. A rectangle should be drawn with four corners and two sets of equal sides. A square should be drawn with four corners and four equal sides.

The correct answer should look like this:

12. Explanation: You can use attributes to draw shapes. A circle should be drawn with no corners or sides. A triangle should be drawn with three sides and three corners. A rectangle should be drawn with four corners and two sets of equal sides. A square should be drawn with four corners and four equal sides.

The correct answer should look like this:

13. Explanation: You can use attributes to draw shapes. A circle should be drawn with no corners or sides. A triangle should be drawn with three sides and three corners. A rectangle should be drawn with four corners and two sets of equal sides. A square should be drawn with four corners and four equal sides.

The correct answer should look like this:

1. Draw a triangle.

Difficulty: Easy

2. Draw two circles that look different. Why are they still circles?

Difficulty: Easy

3. Draw two squares that look different. Why are they still squares?

Difficulty: Easy

4. Draw two rectangles that look different. Why are they still rectangles?

Difficulty: Easy

5. Draw two triangles that look different. Why are they still triangles?

Difficulty: Easy

6. Which shape is a large triangle?

A. C.

B. D.

Difficulty: Easy

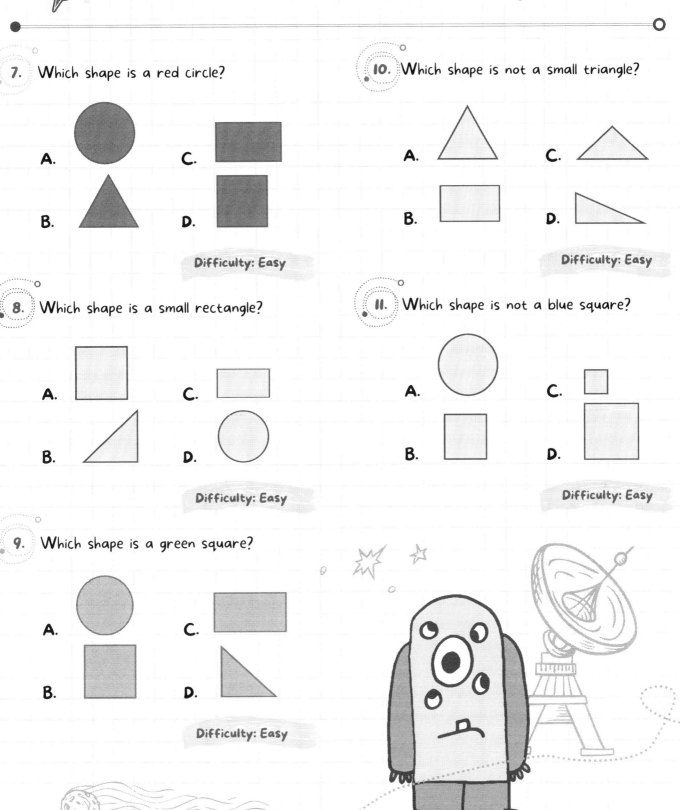

7. Which shape is a red circle?

A.

B.

C.

D.

Difficulty: Easy

8. Which shape is a small rectangle?

A.

B.

C.

D.

Difficulty: Easy

9. Which shape is a green square?

A.

B.

C.

D.

Difficulty: Easy

10. Which shape is not a small triangle?

A.

B.

C.

D.

Difficulty: Easy

11. Which shape is not a blue square?

A.

B.

C.

D.

Difficulty: Easy

1. Explanation: You can use attributes to draw shapes. A circle should be drawn with no corners or sides. A triangle should be drawn with three sides and three corners. A rectangle should be drawn with four corners and two sets of equal sides. A square should be drawn with four corners and four equal sides.

   The correct answer should look like this:

2. Explanation: You can use attributes to draw shapes. A circle should be drawn with no corners or sides. A triangle should be drawn with three sides and three corners. A rectangle should be drawn with four corners and two sets of equal sides. A square should be drawn with four corners and four equal sides. As long as you follow these attributes, it does not

matter what color or size you make your shape. These two circles are circles because they have no corners or sides.

The correct answer should look like this:

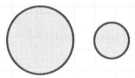

3. Explanation: You can use attributes to draw shapes. A circle should be drawn with no corners or sides. A triangle should be drawn with three sides and three corners. A rectangle should be drawn with four corners and two sets of equal sides. A square should be drawn with four corners and four equal sides. As long as you follow these attributes, it does not matter what color or size you make your shape. These two squares are squares because they have four corners and four equal sides.

The correct answer should look like this:

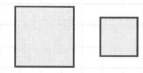

4. Explanation: You can use attributes to draw shapes. A circle should be drawn with no corners or sides. A triangle should be drawn with three sides and three corners. A rectangle should be drawn with four corners and two sets of equal sides. A square should be drawn with four corners and four equal sides. As long as you follow these attributes, it does not matter what color or size you make your shape. These two rectangles are rectangles because they have four corners and two sets of equal sides.

The correct answer should look like this:

5. Explanation: You can use attributes to draw shapes. A circle should be drawn with no corners or sides. A triangle should be drawn with three sides and three corners. A rectangle should be drawn with four corners and two sets of equal sides. A square should be drawn with four corners and four equal sides. As long as you follow these attributes, it does not matter what color or size you make your shape. These two triangles are triangles because they have 3 corners and 3 sides.

The correct answer should look like this:

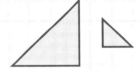

6. Explanation: A circle is a shape with no corners or sides. A triangle is a shape with three sides and three corners. A square is a shape with four corners and four equal sides. A rectangle is a shape with four corners and two sets of equal sides. As long as you follow these attributes, it does not matter what color or size you make your shape. A is the large triangle because it only has 3 sides and 3 corners.

The correct answer is A.

7. Explanation: A circle is a shape with no corners or sides. A triangle is a shape with three sides and three corners. A square is a shape with four corners and four equal sides. A rectangle is a shape with four corners and two sets of equal sides. As long as you follow these attributes, it does not matter what color or size you make your shape. A is the red circle because it has no corners or sides.

The correct answer is A.

8. Explanation: A circle is a shape with no corners or sides. A triangle is a shape with three sides and three corners. A square is a shape with four corners and four equal sides. A rectangle is a shape with four corners and two sets of equal sides. C is the rectangle because it has 4 corners and 2 sets of equal sides.

The correct answer is C.

9. Explanation: A circle is a shape with no corners or sides. A triangle is a shape with three sides and three corners. A square is a shape with four corners and four equal sides. A rectangle is a shape with four corners and two sets of equal sides. B is the square because it has 4 corners and 4 equal sides.

The correct answer is B.

10. Explanation: A circle is a shape with no corners or sides. A triangle is a shape with three sides and three corners. A square is a shape with four corners and four equal sides. A rectangle is a shape with four corners and two sets of equal sides. B is a rectangle because it has 4 corners and 2 sets of equal sides.

The correct answer is B.

11. Explanation: A circle is a shape with no corners or sides. A triangle is a shape with three sides and three corners. A square is a shape with four corners and four equal sides. A rectangle is a shape with four corners and two sets of equal sides. A is not a square because it does not have 4 equal sides and 4 corners. A is a circle.

The correct answer is A.

1. How many angles does a square have?

A. 0   C. 3

B. 2   D. 4

Difficulty: Medium

2. How many angles does a rectangle have?

A. 5   C. 3

B. 4   D. 2

Difficulty: Medium

3. How many angles does a circle have?

A. 0   C. 2

B. 1   D. 3

Difficulty: Medium

4. How many angles does a triangle have?

A. 4   C. 2

B. 3   D. 1

Difficulty: Medium

5. How many angles does this shape have?

A. 3

B. 0

C. 4

D. 2

Difficulty: Medium

6. How many angles does this shape have?

A. 2   C. 4

B. 3   D. 5

Difficulty: Medium

7. Which shape has 3 angles?

A. Triangle   C. Rectangle

B. Square   D. Circle

Difficulty: Medium

8. Which shape has 0 angles?

A. Triangle   C. Square

B. Circle   D. Rectangle

Difficulty: Medium

241

9. Circle the angles on this shape.

Difficulty: Medium

10. Which shape has at least 1 right angle?

A.

C.

B.

D.

Difficulty: Medium

11. Which shape does not have any right angles?

A. Triangle   C. Circle
B. Square   D. Rectangle

Difficulty: Medium

12. How many right angles does this shape have?

A. 1   C. 3
B. 2   D. 4

Difficulty: Medium

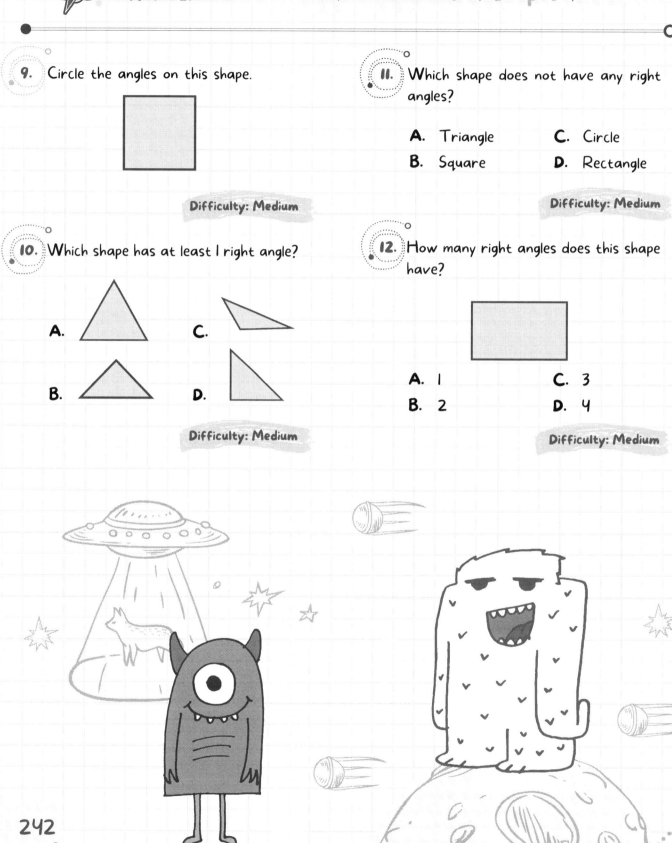

1. Explanation: An angle is a corner where two lines intersect. Shapes have set amount of angles, which is one thing we use to define them as certain types of shape. Circles do not have any angles, triangles always have three angles, and squares and rectangles always have 4 angles.

   The correct answer is D.

2. Explanation: An angle is a corner where two lines intersect. Shapes have set amount of angles, which is one thing we use to define them as certain types of shape. Circles do not have any angles, triangles always have three angles, and squares and rectangles always have 4 angles.

   The correct answer is B.

3. Explanation: An angle is a corner where two lines intersect. Shapes have set amount of angles, which is one thing we use to define them as certain types of shape. Circles do not have any angles, triangles always have three angles, and squares and rectangles always have 4 angles.

   The correct answer is A.

4. Explanation: An angle is a corner where two lines intersect. Shapes have set amount of angles, which is one thing we use to define them as certain types of shape. Circles do not have any angles, triangles always have three angles, and squares and rectangles always have 4 angles.

   The correct answer is B.

5. Explanation: An angle is a corner where two lines intersect. Shapes have set amount of angles, which is one thing we use to define them as certain types of shape. Circles do not have any angles, triangles always have three angles, and squares and rectangles always have 4 angles.

   The correct answer is A.

6. Explanation: An angle is a corner where two lines intersect. Shapes have set amount of angles, which is one thing we use to define them as certain types of shape. Circles do not have any angles, triangles always have three angles, and squares and rectangles always have 4 angles.

   The correct answer is C.

7. Explanation: An angle is a corner where two lines intersect. Shapes have set amount of angles, which is one thing we use to define them as certain types of shape. Circles do not have any angles, triangles always have three angles, and squares and rectangles always have 4 angles.

   The correct answer is A.

8. Explanation: An angle is a corner where two lines intersect. Shapes have set amount of angles, which is one thing we use to define them as certain types of shape. Circles do not have any angles, triangles always have three angles, and squares and rectangles always have 4 angles.

   The correct answer is B.

9. Explanation: An angle is a corner where two lines intersect. Shapes have set amount of angles, which is one thing we use to define them as certain types of shape. Circles do not have any angles, triangles always have three angles, and squares and rectangles always have 4 angles. You should have circled the corners of the square, - those are its angles.

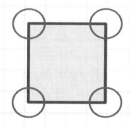

The correct answer should look like this.

10. Explanation: A right angle is where two lines intersect at a **90°** angle. The bottom left corner of triangle D shows two lines meeting in a corner or right angle.

    The correct answer is D.

11. Explanation: A right angle is where two lines intersect at a **90°** angle. Because a circle does not have any lines intersecting in angles or corners, it does not have any right angles.

    The correct answer is C.

12. Explanation: A right angle is where two lines intersect at a **90°** angle. Rectangles have 4 right angles because each corner of a rectangle measures 90°.

    The correct answer is D.

1. How many right angles does this shape have?

A. 4   C. 2
B. 3   D. 1

Difficulty: Medium

2. How many right angles does this shape have?

A. 1   C. 3
B. 2   D. 4

Difficulty: Medium

3. How many right angles does this shape have?

A. 0
B. 1
C. 2
D. 3

Difficulty: Medium

4. How many right angles does a rectangle have?

A. 2   C. 4
B. 1   D. 3

Difficulty: Medium

5. How many right angles does a square have?

A. 1   C. 3
B. 2   D. 4

Difficulty: Medium

6. How many right angles does a circle have?

A. 4   C. 2
B. 0   D. 1

Difficulty: Medium

7. Draw a triangle with a right angle.

Difficulty: Medium

8. Which shape has faces?

A. Circle   **C.** Cylinder
B. Square   **D.** Triangle

Difficulty: Medium

9. Which shape has faces?

A. Rectangle   **C.** Circle
B. Square   **D.** Cube

Difficulty: Medium

10. Which shape has faces?

A.   **C.**
B.   **D.**

Difficulty: Medium

11. Which shape has 2 circle faces?

A.   **C.**
B.   **D.**

Difficulty: Medium

12. How many faces does this shape have?

A. 6   **C.** 4
B. 5   **D.** 3

Difficulty: Medium

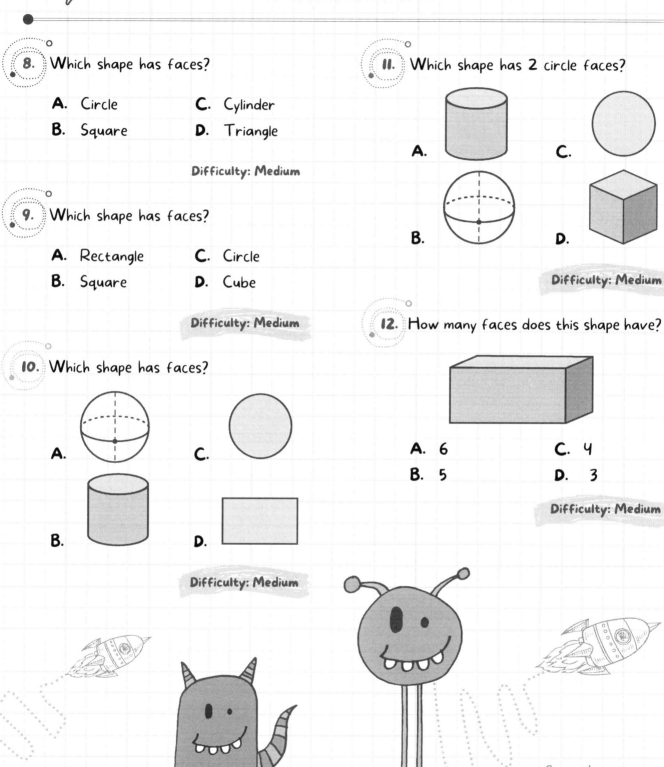

1. Explanation: A right angle is where two lines intersect at a **90°** angle. A triangle can have a right angle, but it does not always need to have a right angle.

   The correct answer is D.

2. Explanation: A right angle is where two lines intersect at a **90°** angle. A shape with 4 sides does not have to have 4 right angles.

   The correct answer is B.

3. Explanation: A right angle is where two lines intersect at a **90°** angle. A circle does not have any right angles.

   The correct answer is A.

4. Explanation: A right angle is where two lines intersect at a **90°** angle. Rectangles have 4 right angles because each corner of a rectangle measures 90°.

   The correct answer is C.

5. Explanation: A right angle is where two lines intersect at a **90°** angle. Squares have 4 right angles because each corner of a square measures 90°.

   The correct answer is D.

6. Explanation: A right angle is where two lines intersect at a **90°** angle. Because a circle does not have any lines intersecting in angles or corners, it does not have any right angles.

   The correct answer is B.

7. Explanation: A right angle is where two lines intersect at a **90°** angle. When drawing a triangle with a right angle, one angle will be a corner and measure **90°** and the other angles will be smaller.

   The correct answer should be a triangle containing 1 right angle.

8. Explanation: 3-Dimensional shapes have faces. A face is the flat surface of any 3D shape. You can think of it as the surface that the shape could sit on. A cylinder is the only choice that is 3D so that is the shape that has faces.

The correct answer is C.

9. Explanation: 3-Dimensional shapes have faces. A face is the flat surface of any 3D shape. You can think of it as the surface that the shape could sit on. A cube is the only choice that is 3D so that is the shape that has faces.

The correct answer is D.

10. Explanation: 3-Dimensional shapes have faces. A face is the flat surface of any 3D shape. You can think of it as the surface that the shape could sit on. While a sphere is 3-dimensional, it does not have any flat surfaces that it can sit on. The only shape shown that has faces is the cylinder.

The correct answer is B.

11. Explanation: 3-Dimensional shapes have faces. A face is the flat surface of any 3D shape. You can think of it as the surface that the shape could sit on. While a sphere is 3-dimensional, it does not have any flat surfaces that it can sit on. Two shapes shown have faces: the circle and the cube. A cylinder has 2 circle shaped faces on the top and the bottom. A cube has 6 square shaped faces.

The correct answer is A.

12. Explanation: 3-Dimensional shapes have faces. A face is the flat surface of any 3D shape. You can think of it as the surface that the shape could sit on. To count the number of faces, you have to remember to account for the back and bottom of the 3-D shape that has faces you cannot currently see.

The correct answer is A.

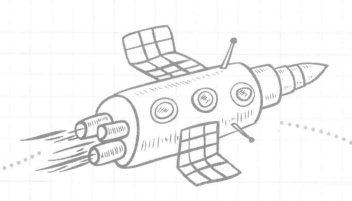

1. How many faces does this shape have?

A. 1   **C.** 3
B. 2   **D.** 4

Difficulty: Medium

2. Which shape does not have any faces?

A.   **C.**

B. 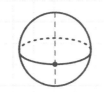   **D.**

Difficulty: Medium

3. Which shape does not have any faces?

A.   **C.**

B. 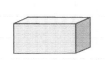   **D.**

Difficulty: Medium

4. Which shape has 6 faces?

A.   **C.**

B.   **D.**

Difficulty: Medium

5. Which shape has 1 circle face?

A.   **C.**

B.   **D.**

Difficulty: Medium

6. Which shape contains 1 rectangular face?

A.   **C.**

B.   **D.**

Difficulty: Medium

7. Which shape has **2 triangular faces?**

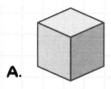
A.

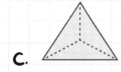
C.

B.

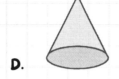
D.

Difficulty: Medium

8. Which shape has **4 faces?**

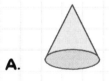
A.

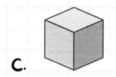
C.

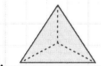
B.

D.

Difficulty: Medium

9. Which shape has **1 curved face?**

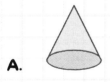
A.

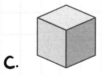
C.

B.

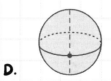
D.

Difficulty: Medium

10. Which shape has **6 faces that are all squares?**

A.

C.

B.

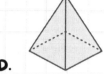
D.

Difficulty: Medium

11. Which shape has **2 circular faces?**

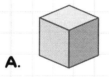
A.

C.

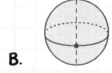
B.

D.

Difficulty: Medium

12. Which shape has **5 faces?**

A.

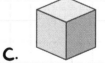
C.

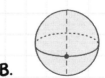
B.

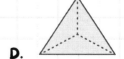
D.

Difficulty: Medium

13. Draw a shape with 6 faces.

Difficulty: Medium

14. Which shape is a quadrilateral?

A.

B.

C.

D.

Difficulty: Hard

15. Which shape is a quadrilateral?

A.

B.

C.

D.

Difficulty: Hard

16. Which shape is not a quadrilateral?

A.

B.

C.

D.

Difficulty: Hard

17. Which shape is not a quadrilateral?

A.

B.

C.

D.

Difficulty: Hard

1. Explanation: 3-Dimensional shapes have faces. A face is the flat surface of any 3D shape. You can think of it as the surface that the shape could sit on. To count the number of faces, you have to remember to account for the back and bottom of the 3-D shape that has faces you cannot currently see. A cylinder has faces at the top and bottom of the shape and then the center is one face that is wrapped around the whole shape.

The correct answer is C.

2. Explanation: 3-Dimensional shapes have faces. A face is the flat surface of any 3D shape. You can think of it as the surface that the shape could sit on. While a sphere is 3-dimensional, it does not have any flat surfaces that it can sit on.

The correct answer is D.

3. Explanation: 3-Dimensional shapes have faces. A face is the flat surface of any 3D shape. You can think of it as the surface that the shape could sit on. A rectangle does not have any faces because it is not 3-dimensional.

The correct answer is C.

4. Explanation: 3-Dimensional shapes have faces. A face is the flat surface of any 3D shape. You can think of it as the surface that the shape could sit on. To count the number of faces, you have to remember to account for the back and bottom of the 3-D shape that has faces you cannot currently see. A cube has six faces, a cylinder 3, a sphere 0, and a pyramid 5.

The correct answer is B.

5. Explanation: 3-Dimensional shapes have faces. A face is the flat surface of any 3D shape. You can think of it as the surface that the shape could sit on. To find the shape with 1 circle face, you have to consider the faces you can and cannot see. A cylinder has 2 circle faces. A sphere does not have any faces. A pyramid does not have any circle faces. A cone has 1 circle face.

The correct answer is C.

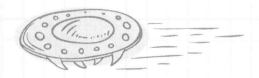

6. Explanation: 3-Dimensional shapes have faces. A face is the flat surface of any 3D shape. You can think of it as the surface that the shape could sit on. To find the shape with 1 rectangular face, you have to consider the faces you can and cannot see. When you unroll a cylinder, you end up with 1 rectangle and 2 circles.

The correct answer is A.

7. Explanation: 3-Dimensional shapes have faces. A face is the flat surface of any 3D shape. You can think of it as the surface that the shape could sit on. To find the shape with 2 triangular faces, you have to consider the faces you can and cannot see. A triangular prism has 2 triangles as faces and the rest of the faces are rectangles.

The correct answer is B.

8. Explanation: 3-Dimensional shapes have faces. A face is the flat surface of any 3D shape. You can think of it as the surface that the shape could sit on. To count the number of faces, you have to remember to account for the back and bottom of the 3-D shape that has faces you cannot currently see. A triangular pyramid has 4 triangular faces. A cone, cube, and sphere have 0 triangles.

The correct answer is B.

9. Explanation: 3-Dimensional shapes have faces. A face is the flat surface of any 3D shape. You can think of it as the surface that the shape could sit on. To find the shape with a curved face, you have to consider the faces you can and cannot see. A cone has a circle face and then a face that will have a curve when you unroll the bottom of the cone.

The correct answer is A.

10. Explanation: 3-Dimensional shapes have faces. A face is the flat surface of any 3D shape. You can think of it as the surface that the shape could sit on. To find the shape with **6** square faces, you have to consider the faces you can and cannot see. A cube has **6** faces that are all squares.

   The correct answer is C.

11. Explanation: 3-Dimensional shapes have faces. A face is the flat surface of any 3D shape. You can think of it as the surface that the shape could sit on. To find the shape with **2** circular faces, you have to consider the faces you can and cannot see. A cylinder has **2** faces that are circles and **1** face that is a rectangle.

   The correct answer is D.

12. Explanation: 3-Dimensional shapes have faces. A face is the flat surface of any 3D shape. You can think of it as the surface that the shape could sit on. To count the number of faces, you have to remember to account for the back and bottom of the 3-D shape that has faces you cannot currently see. A triangular prism has **5** faces.

   The correct answer is A.

13. Explanation: 3-Dimensional shapes have faces. A face is the flat surface of any 3D shape. You can think of it as the surface that the shape could sit on. To draw a shape with the correct number of faces, be sure to count the number of faces, you have to remember to account for the back and bottom of the 3-D shape that has faces you cannot currently see.

   One possible answer could be a cube.

14. Explanation: Any shape with four sides is defined as a quadrilateral. There are many different types of quadrilaterals. A trapezoid is a quadrilateral with two parallel sides. A rhombus is a quadrilateral with 4 equal sides and opposite sides parallel. A rhombus with 4 90° angles is a square. A parallelogram has opposite sides parallel and equal. A parallelogram with 4 90° angles is a rectangle.

The correct answer is B.

16. Explanation: Any shape with four sides is defined as a quadrilateral. There are many different types of quadrilaterals. A trapezoid is a quadrilateral with two parallel sides. A rhombus is a quadrilateral with 4 equal sides and opposite sides parallel. A rhombus with 4 90° angles is a square. A parallelogram has opposite sides parallel and equal. A parallelogram with 4 90° angles is a rectangle.

The correct answer is A.

15. Explanation: Any shape with four sides is defined as a quadrilateral. There are many different types of quadrilaterals. A trapezoid is a quadrilateral with two parallel sides. A rhombus is a quadrilateral with 4 equal sides and opposite sides parallel. A rhombus with 4 90° angles is a square. A parallelogram has opposite sides parallel and equal. A parallelogram with 4 90° angles is a rectangle.

The correct answer is C.

17. Explanation: Any shape with four sides is defined as a quadrilateral. There are many different types of quadrilaterals. A trapezoid is a quadrilateral with two parallel sides. A rhombus is a quadrilateral with 4 equal sides and opposite sides parallel. A rhombus with 4 90° angles is a square. A parallelogram has opposite sides parallel and equal. A parallelogram with 4 90° angles is a rectangle.

The correct answer is A.

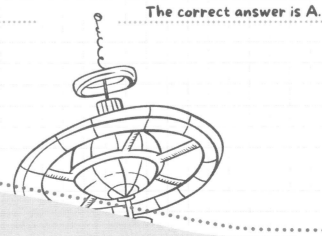

1. Which shape is a trapezoid?

A.

C.

B.

D.

Difficulty: Hard

2. Which shape is not a trapezoid?

A.

C.

B.

D.

Difficulty: Hard

3. Which shape is not a rhombus?

A.

C.

B.

D.

Difficulty: Hard

4. Which shape is a rhombus?

A.

C.

B.

D.

Difficulty: Hard

5. Which shape is not a square?

A.

C.

B.

D.

Difficulty: Hard

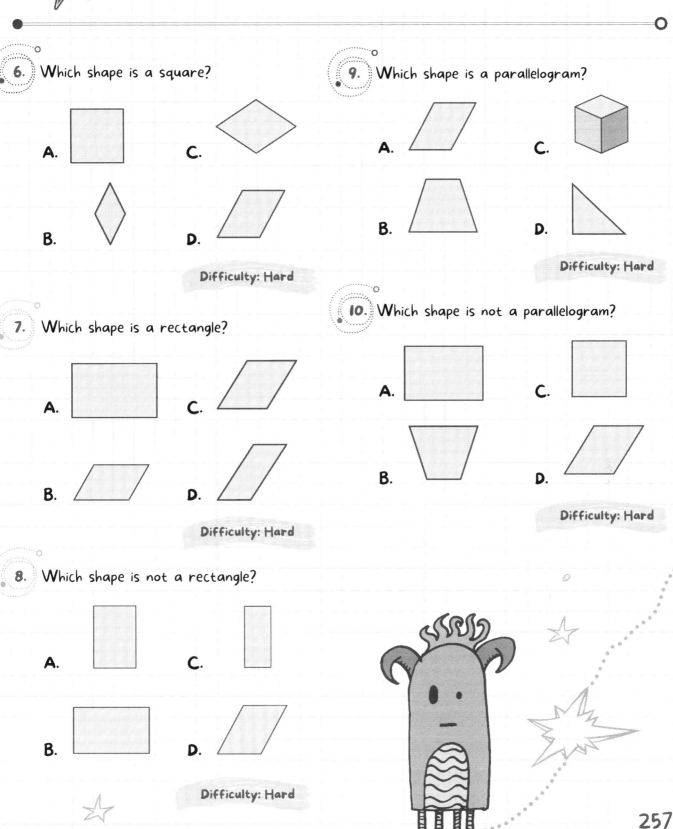

6. Which shape is a square?

A.

B.

C.

D.

Difficulty: Hard

7. Which shape is a rectangle?

A.

B.

C.

D.

Difficulty: Hard

8. Which shape is not a rectangle?

A.

B.

C.

D.

Difficulty: Hard

9. Which shape is a parallelogram?

A.

B.

C.

D.

Difficulty: Hard

10. Which shape is not a parallelogram?

A.

B.

C.

D.

Difficulty: Hard

11. When this shape is complete, what will it be?

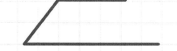

A. Trapezoid
B. Square
C. Rectangle
D. Parallelogram

Difficulty: Hard

12. When this shape is complete, what will it be?

A. Triangle
C. Square
B. Cube
D. Trapezoid

Difficulty: Hard

13. When this shape is complete, what will it be?

A. Trapezoid
B. Square
C. Rectangle
D. Parallelogram

Difficulty: Hard

14. When this shape is complete, what will it be?

A. Square
C. Rectangle
B. Rhombus
D. Trapezoid

Difficulty: Hard

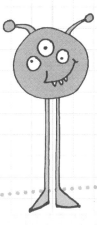

1. Explanation: Any shape with four sides is defined as a quadrilateral. There are many different types of quadrilaterals. A trapezoid is a quadrilateral with two parallel sides. A rhombus is a quadrilateral with 4 equal sides and opposite sides parallel. A rhombus with 4 90° angles is a square. A parallelogram has opposite sides parallel and equal. A parallelogram with 4 90° angles is a rectangle.

   The correct answer is D.

2. Explanation: Any shape with four sides is defined as a quadrilateral. There are many different types of quadrilaterals. A trapezoid is a quadrilateral with two parallel sides. A rhombus is a quadrilateral with 4 equal sides and opposite sides parallel. A rhombus with 4 90° angles is a square. A parallelogram has opposite sides parallel and equal. A parallelogram with 4 90° angles is a rectangle.

   The correct answer is C.

3. Explanation: Any shape with four sides is defined as a quadrilateral. There are many different types of quadrilaterals. A trapezoid is a quadrilateral with two parallel sides. A rhombus is a quadrilateral with 4 equal sides and opposite sides parallel. A rhombus is a shape with four equal sides. A parallelogram has opposite sides parallel and equal. A parallelogram with 4 90° angles is a rectangle.

   The correct answer is D.

4. Explanation: Any shape with four sides is defined as a quadrilateral. There are many different types of quadrilaterals. A trapezoid is a quadrilateral with two parallel sides. A rhombus is a quadrilateral with 4 equal sides and opposite sides parallel. A rhombus with 4 90° angles is a square. A parallelogram has opposite sides parallel and equal. A parallelogram with 4 90° angles is a rectangle.

   The correct answer is C.

5. Explanation: Any shape with four sides is defined as a quadrilateral. There are many different types of quadrilaterals. A trapezoid is a quadrilateral with two parallel sides. A rhombus is a quadrilateral with 4 equal sides and opposite sides parallel. A rhombus with 4 90° angles is a square. A parallelogram has opposite sides parallel and equal. A parallelogram with 4 90° angles is a rectangle.

The correct answer is D.

6. Explanation: Any shape with four sides is defined as a quadrilateral. There are many different types of quadrilaterals. A trapezoid is a quadrilateral with two parallel sides. A rhombus is a quadrilateral with 4 equal sides and opposite sides parallel. A rhombus with 4 90° angles is a square. A parallelogram has opposite sides parallel and equal. A parallelogram with 4 90° angles is a rectangle.

The correct answer is A.

7. Explanation: Any shape with four sides is defined as a quadrilateral. There are many different types of quadrilaterals. A trapezoid is a quadrilateral with two parallel sides. A rhombus is a quadrilateral with 4 equal sides and opposite sides parallel. A rhombus with 4 90° angles is a square. A parallelogram has opposite sides parallel and equal. A parallelogram with 4 90° angles is a rectangle.

The correct answer is A.

8. Explanation: Any shape with four sides is defined as a quadrilateral. There are many different types of quadrilaterals. A trapezoid is a quadrilateral with two parallel sides. A rhombus is a quadrilateral with 4 equal sides and opposite sides parallel. A rhombus with 4 90° angles is a square. A parallelogram has opposite sides parallel and equal. A parallelogram with 4 90° angles is a rectangle.

The correct answer is D.

9. Explanation: Any shape with four sides is defined as a quadrilateral. There are many different types of quadrilaterals. A trapezoid is a quadrilateral with two parallel sides. A rhombus is a quadrilateral with 4 equal sides and opposite sides parallel. A rhombus with 4 90° angles is a square. A parallelogram has opposite sides parallel and equal. A parallelogram with 4 90° angles is a rectangle.

The correct answer is A.

10. Explanation: Any shape with four sides is defined as a quadrilateral. There are many different types of quadrilaterals. A trapezoid is a quadrilateral with two parallel sides. A rhombus is a quadrilateral with 4 equal sides and opposite sides parallel. A rhombus with 4 90° angles is a square. A parallelogram has opposite sides parallel and equal. A parallelogram with 4 90° angles is a rectangle.

The correct answer is B.

11. Explanation: Drawing the missing line will give you a shape with two parallel sides. A trapezoid is a quadrilateral with two parallel sides.

The correct answer is A.

12. Explanation: Drawing the missing line will give you a shape with four equal, parallel sides with 90° angles or a square.

The correct answer is C.

13. Explanation: Drawing the missing line will give you a shape with opposite sides parallel and equal or a parallelogram.

The correct answer is D.

14. Explanation: Drawing the missing line will give you a quadrilateral with 2 sets of equal sides all at 90° angles.

The correct answer is C.

1. What is this shape?

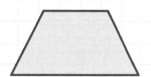

A. Rectangle **C.** Trapezoid
B. Square **D.** Triangle

Difficulty: Easy

2. What is this shape?

A. Rectangle **C.** Trapezoid
B. Square **D.** Triangle

Difficulty: Easy

3. What is this shape?

A. Rectangle **C.** Trapezoid
B. Square **D.** Triangle

Difficulty: Easy

4. What is this shape?

A. Rectangle **C.** Trapezoid
B. Square **D.** Triangle

Difficulty: Easy

5. What is this shape?

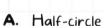

A. Half-circle
B. Circle
C. Quarter-circle
D. Part-circle

Difficulty: Easy

6. What is this shape?

A. Half-circle
B. Circle
C. Quarter-circle
D. Part-circle

Difficulty: Easy

7. What is this shape?

A. Half-circle
B. Circle
C. Quarter-circle
D. Part-circle

Difficulty: Easy

8. Which shape is not a rectangle?

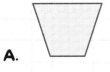

A.   **C.**

B.   **D.**

Difficulty: Easy

9. Which shape is not a square?

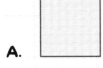

A.   **C.**

B.   **D.**

Difficulty: Easy

10. Which shape is not a triangle?

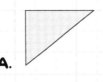

A.   **C.**

B.   **D.**

Difficulty: Easy

11. Which shape is not a trapezoid?

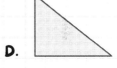

A.   **C.**

B.   **D.**

Difficulty: Easy

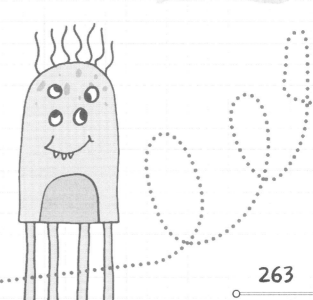

1. Explanation: A rectangle is a shape with two sets of equal sides. A square is a shape with four equal sides. A trapezoid is a shape with two sides that go in the same direction and do not touch (parallel). A triangle is a shape that has three equal sides. This shape has two sides that go in the same direction and do not touch, so it is a trapezoid.

   The correct answer is C.

2. Explanation: A rectangle is a shape with two sets of equal sides. A square is a shape with four equal sides. A trapezoid is a shape with two sides that go in the same direction and do not touch (parallel). A triangle is a shape that has three equal sides. This shape has four equal sides, so it is a square.

   The correct answer is B.

3. Explanation: A rectangle is a shape with two sets of equal sides. A square is a shape with four equal sides. A trapezoid is a shape with two sides that go in the same direction and do not touch (parallel). A triangle is a shape that has three equal sides. This shape has two sets of equal sides, so it is a rectangle.

   The correct answer is A.

4. Explanation: A rectangle is a shape with two sets of equal sides. A square is a shape with four equal sides. A trapezoid is a shape with two sides that go in the same direction and do not touch (parallel). A triangle is a shape that has three equal sides. This shape has three sides so it is a triangle.

   The correct answer is D.

5. Explanation: A circle is a round shape with no beginning or end. A half-circle is a shape that shows a part of a circle cut into 2 equal parts. A quarter-circle is a shape that shows a part of a circle cut into 4 equal parts. This is a round shape with no beginning or end, so it is a circle.

   The correct answer is B.

6. Explanation: A circle is a round shape with no beginning or end. A half-circle is a shape that shows a part of a circle cut into 2 equal parts. A quarter-circle is a shape that shows a part of a circle cut into 4 equal parts. This shape shows a part of a circle that has been cut into 4 equal parts, so it is a quarter-circle.

The correct answer is C.

7. Explanation: A circle is a round shape with no beginning or end. A half-circle is a shape that shows a part of a circle cut into 2 equal parts. A quarter-circle is a shape that shows a part of a circle cut into 4 equal parts. This shape shows a part of a circle that has been cut into 2 equal parts, so it is a half-circle.

The correct answer is A.

8. Explanation: A rectangle is a shape with two sets of equal sides. A square is a shape with four equal sides. A trapezoid is a shape with two sides that go in the same direction and do not touch (parallel). A triangle is a shape that has three equal sides. Choice A is the only shape that does not have two sets of equal sides.

The correct answer is A.

9. Explanation: A rectangle is a shape with two sets of equal sides. A square is a shape with four equal sides. A trapezoid is a shape with two sides that go in the same direction and do not touch (parallel). A triangle is a shape that has three equal sides. Shape D is the only shape that does not have four equal sides.

The correct answer is D.

10. Explanation: A rectangle is a shape with two sets of equal sides. A square is a shape with four equal sides. A trapezoid is a shape with two sides that go in the same direction and do not touch (parallel). A triangle is a shape that has three equal sides. Shape B is the only shape that does not have three sides.

The correct answer is B.

11. Explanation: A rectangle is a shape with two sets of equal sides. A square is a shape with four equal sides. A trapezoid is a shape with two sides that go in the same direction and do not touch (parallel). A triangle is a shape that has three equal sides. Shape D is the only shape that does not have four sides with two that go in the same direction and do not touch.

The correct answer is D.

1. Which shape is not a part of a circle?

A.

C.

B.

D.

Difficulty: Easy

2. Draw a rectangle.

Difficulty: Easy

3. Draw a square.

Difficulty: Easy

4. Draw a trapezoid.

Difficulty: Easy

5. Draw a triangle.

Difficulty: Easy

6. Draw a half-circle.

Difficulty: Easy

7. What is this shape?

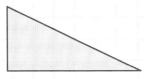

A. Triangle
B. Quadrilateral
C. Pentagon
D. Hexagon

Difficulty: Medium

8. What is this shape?

A. Triangle
B. Quadrilateral
C. Pentagon
D. Hexagon

Difficulty: Medium

9. What is this shape?

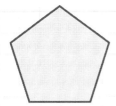

A. Triangle
B. Quadrilateral
C. Pentagon
D. Hexagon

Difficulty: Medium

10. What is this shape?

A. Triangle
B. Quadrilateral
C. Pentagon
D. Hexagon

Difficulty: Medium

11. What is this shape?

A. Triangle
B. Quadrilateral
C. Pentagon
D. Hexagon

Difficulty: Medium

12. What is this shape?

A. Triangle
B. Quadrilateral
C. Pentagon
D. Hexagon

Difficulty: Medium

1. Explanation: A circle is a round shape with no beginning or end. A half-circle is a shape that shows a part of a circle cut into **2** equal parts. A quarter-circle is a shape that shows a part of a circle cut into **4** equal parts. Choice D is a full circle, not a circle cut into parts.

   The correct answer is D.

2. Explanation: To draw a rectangle, you should draw a shape with two sets of equal sides.

   Students should draw a shape with two sets of equal, parallel sides.

3. Explanation: To draw a square, you should draw a shape with four equal sides.

   Students should draw a shape with four equal sides.

4. Explanation: To draw a trapezoid, you should draw a shape with two sides that go in the same direction and do not touch (parallel).

   Students should draw a shape with two sides that go in the same direction and do not touch.

5. Explanation: To draw a triangle, you should draw a shape with three sides.

   Students should draw a shape with three sides.

6. Explanation: To draw a half-circle, you should draw a shape that shows one part of a circle that is divided into two equal parts.

   Students should draw a shape that represents one part of a circle divided into two equal parts.

7. Explanation: A triangle is a shape with three sides. A quadrilateral is a shape with four sides. A pentagon is a shape with five sides. A hexagon is a shape with six sides. This shape has three sides so it is a triangle.

The correct answer is A.

8. Explanation: A triangle is a shape with three sides. A quadrilateral is a shape with four sides. A pentagon is a shape with five sides. A hexagon is a shape with six sides. This shape has four sides so it is a quadrilateral.

The correct answer is B.

9. Explanation: A triangle is a shape with three sides. A quadrilateral is a shape with four sides. A pentagon is a shape with five sides. A hexagon is a shape with six sides. This shape has five sides so it is a pentagon.

The correct answer is C.

10. Explanation: A triangle is a shape with three sides. A quadrilateral is a shape with four sides. A pentagon is a shape with five sides. A hexagon is a shape with six sides. This shape has six sides so it is a hexagon.

The correct answer is D.

11. Explanation: A triangle is a shape with three sides. A quadrilateral is a shape with four sides. A pentagon is a shape with five sides. A hexagon is a shape with six sides. This shape has three sides so it is a triangle.

The correct answer is A.

12. Explanation: A triangle is a shape with three sides. A quadrilateral is a shape with four sides. A pentagon is a shape with five sides. A hexagon is a shape with six sides. This shape has four sides so it is a quadrilateral.

The correct answer is B.

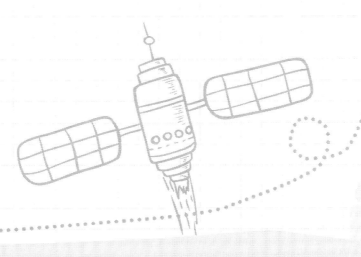

1. What is this shape?

A. Triangle
B. Quadrilateral
C. Pentagon
D. Hexagon

Difficulty: Medium

2. What is this shape?

A. Triangle
B. Quadrilateral
C. Pentagon
D. Hexagon

Difficulty: Medium

3. Which shape is a triangle?

A.   C.

B.   D.

Difficulty: Medium

4. Which shape is a pentagon?

A.   C.

B.   D.

Difficulty: Medium

5. Which shape is a quadrilateral?

A.   C.

B.   D.

Difficulty: Medium

6. Which shape is a hexagon?

A.   C.

B.   D.

Difficulty: Medium

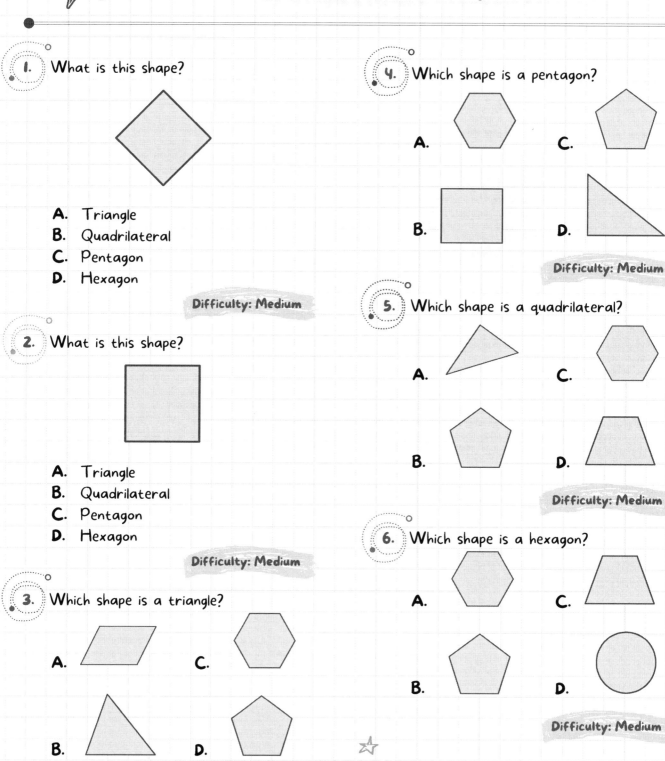

7. Which shape is not a pentagon?

A.

C.

B.

D.

Difficulty: Medium

8. Which shape is a hexagon?

A.

C.

B.

D.

Difficulty: Medium

9. How many sides does a hexagon have?

A. 3   C. 5
B. 4   D. 6

Difficulty: Medium

10. How many sides does a pentagon have?

A. 3   C. 5
B. 4   D. 6

Difficulty: Medium

11. Draw a pentagon.

Difficulty: Medium

12. Draw a hexagon.

Difficulty: Medium

1. Explanation: A triangle is a shape with three sides. A quadrilateral is a shape with four sides. A pentagon is a shape with five sides. A hexagon is a shape with six sides. This shape has four sides so it is a quadrilateral.

   The correct answer is B.

2. Explanation: A triangle is a shape with three sides. A quadrilateral is a shape with four sides. A pentagon is a shape with five sides. A hexagon is a shape with six sides. This shape has four sides so it is a quadrilateral.

   The correct answer is B.

3. Explanation: A triangle is a shape with three sides. A quadrilateral is a shape with four sides. A pentagon is a shape with five sides. A hexagon is a shape with six sides. Choice B is the only shape with three sides so it is the triangle.

   The correct answer is B.

4. Explanation: A triangle is a shape with three sides. A quadrilateral is a shape with four sides. A pentagon is a shape with five sides. A hexagon is a shape with six sides. Choice C is the only shape with five sides so it is the pentagon.

   The correct answer is C.

5. Explanation: A triangle is a shape with three sides. A quadrilateral is a shape with four sides. A pentagon is a shape with five sides. A hexagon is a shape with six sides. Choice D is the only shape with four sides so it is the quadrilateral.

   The correct answer is D.

6. Explanation: A triangle is a shape with three sides. A quadrilateral is a shape with four sides. A pentagon is a shape with five sides. A hexagon is a shape with six sides. Choice A has six sides so it is the hexagon.

   The correct answer is A.

7. Explanation: A triangle is a shape with three sides. A quadrilateral is a shape with four sides. A pentagon is a shape with five sides. A hexagon is a shape with six sides. Choice B is the only choice that does not have **5** sides, so it is not a pentagon.

The correct answer is B.

8. Explanation: A triangle is a shape with three sides. A quadrilateral is a shape with four sides. A pentagon is a shape with five sides. A hexagon is a shape with six sides. Choice B is the only choice that has six sides, so it is a hexagon.

The correct answer is B.

9. Explanation: A triangle is a shape with three sides. A quadrilateral is a shape with four sides. A pentagon is a shape with five sides. A hexagon is a shape with six sides..

The correct answer is D.

10. Explanation: A triangle is a shape with three sides. A quadrilateral is a shape with four sides. A pentagon is a shape with five sides. A hexagon is a shape with six sides.

The correct answer is C.

11. Explanation: To draw a pentagon, you should draw a shape with five sides.

Students should draw a shape with five sides.

12. Explanation: To draw a hexagon, you should draw a shape with six sides.

Students should draw a shape with six sides.

1. Which shape is a polygon?

A. C.

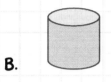

B. D.

Difficulty: Hard

2. Which shape is a polygon?

A. C.

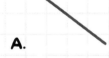

B. D.

Difficulty: Hard

3. Which shape is not a polygon?

A. C.

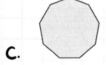

B. D.

Difficulty: Hard

4. Which shape is not a polygon?

 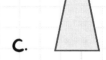

A. C.

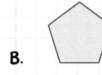 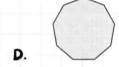

B. D.

Difficulty: Hard

5. Which shape always has one pair of parallel sides?

A. Triangle
B. Polygon
C. Trapezoid
D. Cone

Difficulty: Hard

6. Which shape has two parallel sets of sides and 2 sets of equal sides?

A. Pentagon
B. Triangle
C. Trapezoid
D. Rhombus

Difficulty: Hard

7. Which shape has no parallel lines?

A. Square
B. Rectangle
C. Circles
D. Trapezoid

Difficulty: Hard

8. Which shape can have **2** pairs of parallel sides?

A. Triangle
B. Circle
C. Parallelogram
D. Trapezoid

Difficulty: Hard

9. Which shape must have 4 equal angles?

A. Circle
B. Triangle
C. Quadrilateral
D. Rectangle

Difficulty: Hard

10. Which shape has 4 equal sides and angles?

A. Triangle
B. Square
C. Trapezoid
D. Parallelogram

Difficulty: Hard

11. Draw a quadrilateral that has no parallel sides.

Difficulty: Hard

12. Draw a quadrilateral that has one set of equal sides.

Difficulty: Hard

13. Draw a quadrilateral that has two sets of parallel sides.

Difficulty: Hard

275

14. Draw a quadrilateral that has two sets of equal sides.

Difficulty: Hard

15. Draw a quadrilateral that has 4 90° angles.

Difficulty: Hard

16. Draw a quadrilateral that has 1 set of parallel sides.

Difficulty: Hard

17. Draw a rhombus.

Difficulty: Hard

18. Draw a parallelogram.

Difficulty: Hard

1. Explanation: A polygon is a 2-dimensional figure with at least three straight sides and angles, usually having more than five sides. Shape D is a polygon because it has seven sides.

   The correct answer is D.

2. Explanation: A polygon is a 2-dimensional figure with at least three straight sides and angles, usually having more than five sides. Shape C is a polygon because it has nine sides.

   The correct answer is C.

3. Explanation: A polygon is a 2-dimensional figure with at least three straight sides and angles, usually having more than five sides. Shape B is not a polygon because it does not have three straight sides and angles.

   The correct answer is B.

4. Explanation: A polygon is a 2-dimensional figure with at least three straight sides and angles, usually having more than five sides. Shape A is not a polygon because it is 3-dimensional.

   The correct answer is A.

5. Explanation: A trapezoid is a shape with four sides that has one pair of parallel sides.

   The correct answer is C.

6. Explanation: A rhombus is a shape that has four sides with two parallel sets of sides and two sets of equal sides.

   The correct answer is D.

7. Explanation: A square has two pairs of parallel lines. A rectangle also has two pairs of parallel lines. A trapezoid has one pair of parallel lines. A circle does not have any parallel lines.

   The correct answer is C.

8. Explanation: A parallelogram has two pairs of parallel sides. A trapezoid only has 1 set of parallel sides, while triangles and circles do not have any parallel sides.

   The correct answer is C.

9. Explanation: A rectangle has four equal angles all of which measure 90°.

   The correct answer is D.

10. Explanation: A square must have four equal sides all of which measure 90°.

    The correct answer is B.

11. Explanation: A quadrilateral is a shape with four sides. You should have drawn a shape with four sides that are not equal distance from each other.

    Students should draw a four sided shape with no parallel sides.

12. Explanation: A quadrilateral is a shape with four sides. You should have drawn a shape with one set of equal sides. You could have drawn a trapezoid.

    Students should draw a four sided shape with one set of equal sides.

13. Explanation: A quadrilateral is a shape with four sides. You should have drawn a shape with two sets of parallel sides. You could have drawn a parallelogram or a rectangle.

    Students should draw a four sided shape with two sets of parallel sides.

14. Explanation: A quadrilateral is a shape with four sides. You should have drawn a shape with two sets of equal sides.

    Students should draw a four sided shape with two sets of equal sides (a rectangle).

15. Explanation: A quadrilateral is a shape with four sides. You should have drawn a shape with 4 90° angles.

    Students should draw a four sided shape with 4 90° angles (a rectangle or a square).

16. Explanation: A quadrilateral is a shape with four sides. You should have drawn a shape with with 1 set of parallel sides.

    Students should draw a four sided shape with 1 set of parallel sides.

17. Explanation: A rhombus is a shape with four sides that are equal and equal opposite angles.

    Students should draw a four sided shape with equal opposite angles and four equal sides.

18. Explanation: A parallelogram is a shape with opposite sides parallel.
    Students should draw a four sided shape with opposite sides parallel.

1. What is this shape?

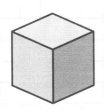

A. Cube   C. Cone
B. Prism   D. Cylinder

Difficulty: Easy

2. What is this shape?

A. Cube   C. Cone
B. Prism   D. Cylinder

Difficulty: Easy

3. What is this shape?

A. Cube   C. Cone
B. Prism   D. Cylinder

Difficulty: Easy

4. What is this shape?

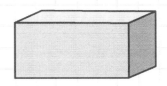

A. Cube   C. Cone
B. Prism   D. Cylinder

Difficulty: Easy

5. Which shape is a cube?

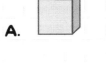

A.   C.

B.   D.

Difficulty: Easy

6. Which shape is not a cube?

A.   C.

B.   D.

Difficulty: Easy

7. Which shape is a prism?

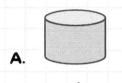 A.

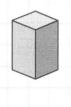 C.

 B.

D.

Difficulty: Easy

8. Which shape is not a prism?

A.

C.

B.

D.

Difficulty: Easy

9. Which shape is a cone?

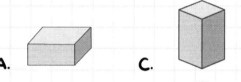 A.

C.

 B.

 D.

Difficulty: Easy

10. Which shape is not a cone?

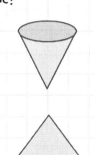 A.

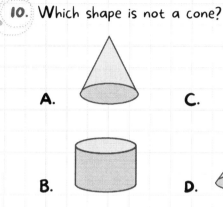 C.

B.

D.

Difficulty: Easy

11. Which shape is a cylinder?

A.

 C.

B.

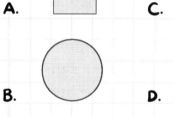 D.

Difficulty: Easy

12. Which shape is not a cylinder?

 A.

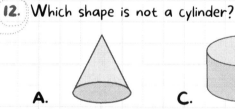 C.

 B.

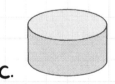 D.

Difficulty: Easy

1. Explanation: A cube is formed with six faces that are squares. A right rectangular prism has six faces that are rectangles, two of which may be squares. A cone is a shape that has a circle face and a curved bottom that comes to a point. A cylinder is a shape that has two circular bases and a rectangle curved middle that connects the two. This shape has six faces that are squares so it is a cube.

The correct answer is A.

2. Explanation: A cube is formed with six faces that are squares. A right rectangular prism has six faces that are rectangles, two of which may be squares. A cone is a shape that has a circle face and a curved bottom that comes to a point. A cylinder is a shape that has two circular bases and a rectangle curved middle that connects the two. This shape has two circular bases, so it is a cylinder.

The correct answer is D.

3. Explanation: A cube is formed with six faces that are squares. A right rectangular prism has six faces that are rectangles, two of which may be squares. A cone is a shape that has a circle face and a curved bottom that comes to a point. A cylinder is a shape that has two circular bases and a rectangle curved middle that connects the two. This shape has a circle face and a curved bottom so it is a cone.

The correct answer is C.

4. Explanation: A cube is formed with six faces that are squares. A right rectangular prism has six faces that are rectangles, two of which may be squares. A cone is a shape that has a circle face and a curved bottom that comes to a point. A cylinder is a shape that has two circular bases and a rectangle curved middle that connects the two. This shape has six faces that are rectangles so it is a prism.

The correct answer is B.

5. Explanation: A cube is formed with six faces that are squares. A right rectangular prism has six faces that are rectangles, two of which may be squares. A cone is a shape that has a circle face and a curved bottom that comes to a point. A cylinder is a shape that has two circular bases and a rectangle curved middle that connects the two. Choice D is the only shape that has six faces that are squares, the rest contain rectangles.

The correct answer is D.

6. Explanation: A cube is formed with six faces that are squares. A right rectangular prism has six faces that are rectangles, two of which may be squares. A cone is a shape that has a circle face and a curved bottom that comes to a point. A cylinder is a shape that has two circular bases and a rectangle curved middle that connects the two. Choice B is the only shape that does not have six faces that are squares so it is not a cube.

The correct answer is B.

7. Explanation: A cube is formed with six faces that are squares. A right rectangular prism has six faces that are rectangles, two of which may be squares. A cone is a shape that has a circle face and a curved bottom that comes to a point. A cylinder is a shape that has two circular bases and a rectangle curved middle that connects the two. Choice C is the only choice that has six faces that are rectangles.

The correct answer is C.

8. Explanation: A cube is formed with six faces that are squares. A right rectangular prism has six faces that are rectangles, two of which may be squares. A cone is a shape that has a circle face and a curved bottom that comes to a point. A cylinder is a shape that has two circular bases and a rectangle curved middle that connects the two. Choice D is not a prism.

The correct answer is D.

9. Explanation: A cube is formed with six faces that are squares. A right rectangular prism has six faces that are rectangles, two of which may be squares. A cone is a shape that has a circle face and a curved bottom that comes to a point. A cylinder is a shape that has two circular bases and a rectangle curved middle that connects the two. Choice A is the only choice that has a circular face and a curved bottom that comes to a point.

The correct answer is A.

10. Explanation: A cube is formed with six faces that are squares. A right rectangular prism has six faces that are rectangles, two of which may be squares. A cone is a shape that has a circle face and a curved bottom that comes to a point. A cylinder is a shape that has two circular bases and a rectangle curved middle that connects the two. Choice B is the only choice that does not have 1 circle face that comes to a point.

The correct answer is B.

11. Explanation: A cube is formed with six faces that are squares. A right rectangular prism has six faces that are rectangles, two of which may be squares. A cone is a shape that has a circle face and a curved bottom that comes to a point. A cylinder is a shape that has two circular bases and a rectangle curved middle that connects the two. Choice C is the only choice that contains two circular bases and a rectangle middle that connects the two. Choices A and B are not 3D shapes.

The correct answer is C.

12. Explanation: A cube is formed with six faces that are squares. A right rectangular prism has six faces that are rectangles, two of which may be squares. A cone is a shape that has a circle face and a curved bottom that comes to a point. A cylinder is a shape that has two circular bases and a rectangle curved middle that connects the two. Choice A is the only choice that has one circular base and comes to point and is a cone. The other shapes have 2 circular bases connected by a rectangle and are cylinders.

The correct answer is A.

1. What is this shape?

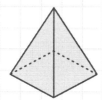

A. Circle   **C.** Square

B. Sphere   **D.** Pyramid

Difficulty: Medium

2. What is this shape?

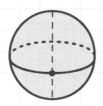

A. Circle   **C.** Square

B. Sphere   **D.** Pyramid

Difficulty: Medium

3. Which shape is a sphere in real life?

A. A globe

B. A can of soda

C. A traffic cone

D. A book

Difficulty: Medium

4. Which shape is a sphere in real life?

A. A shoebox

B. An ice cream cone

C. A basketball

D. A map

Difficulty: Medium

5. Which shape is a pyramid?

A.   **C.**

B.   **D.**

Difficulty: Medium

6. Which shape is a pyramid?

A.   **C.**

B.   **D.**

Difficulty: Medium

7. Which shape is not a pyramid?

A.

B.

C.

D.

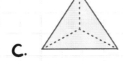

Difficulty: Medium

8. Which shape is not a sphere in real life?

A. Gumball   C. Marble

B. Tissue box   D. Soccer ball

Difficulty: Medium

9. What shape is the base of a cylinder?

A. Circle
B. Square
C. Triangle
D. Rectangle

Difficulty: Medium

10. What shape is the base of a cube?

A. Circle   C. Triangle

B. Square   D. Rectangle

Difficulty: Medium

11. What shape is the base of the following pyramid?

A. Circle   C. Triangle

B. Square   D. Rectangle

Difficulty: Medium

12. What shape is the base of a cone?

A. Rectangle
B. Square
C. Circle
D. Triangle

Difficulty: Medium

13. Which shape is a rectangular prism?

A.

C.

B.

D.

Difficulty: Medium

1. Explanation: A sphere is a shape that is round, which no flat bases. A pyramid is a shape with a base that is usually a square or triangle that comes to a point. A circle and a square are not 3-dimenisonal shapes.

   The correct answer is D.

2. Explanation: A sphere is a shape that is round, which no flat bases. A pyramid is a shape with a base that is usually a square or triangle that comes to a point. A circle and a square are not 3-dimenisonal shapes.

   The correct answer is B.

3. Explanation: A sphere is a shape that is round, which no flat bases. A globe is a sphere that occurs in real life.

   The correct answer is A.

4. Explanation: A sphere is a shape that is round, which no flat bases. A basketball is a sphere that occurs in real life.

   The correct answer is C.

5. Explanation: Choice C is a shape with a triangle base that comes to a point, so it is a pyramid. Choice A is a triangle, choice B is a prism, and choice D is a cone.

   The correct answer is C.

6. Explanation: Choice D is a shape with a square base that comes to a point, so it is a pyramid. Choice A is a prism, choice B is a triangle, and choice C is a prism.

   The correct answer is D.

7. Explanation: Choice D is the only choice that does not come to a point.

    The correct answer is D.

8. Explanation: The only choice that is not a round object with no flat base is a tissue box.

    The correct answer is B.

9. Explanation: The base of a shape is the surface or bottom that an object rests on. It can be the bottom but it can also be the top. The base of a cylinder is a circle.

    The correct answer is A.

10. Explanation: The base of a shape is the surface or bottom that an object rests on. It can be the bottom but it can also be the top. The base of a cube is a square.

    The correct answer is B.

11. Explanation: The base of a shape is the surface or bottom that an object rests on. It can be the bottom but it can also be the top. The base of the pyramid is a triangle.

    The correct answer is C.

12. Explanation: The base of a shape is the surface or bottom that an object rests on. It can be the bottom but it can also be the top. The base of the cone is a circle.

    The correct answer is C.

13. Explanation: A rectangular prism has six faces and has two bases that are rectangles. A rectangular prism can also have two bases that are squares that are connected by rectangles.

    The correct answer is B.

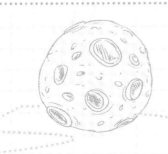

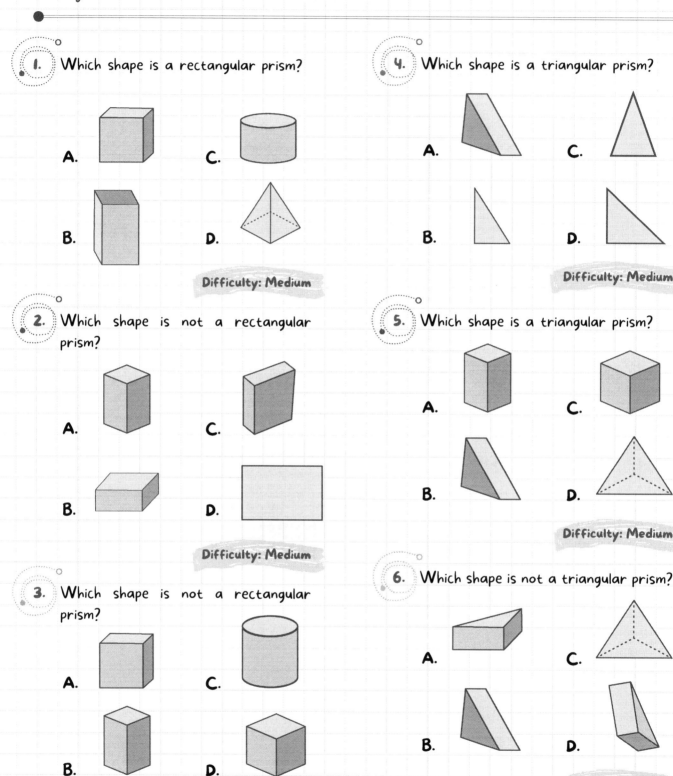

1. Which shape is a rectangular prism?

A.

C.

B.

D.

Difficulty: Medium

2. Which shape is not a rectangular prism?

A.

C.

B.

D.

Difficulty: Medium

3. Which shape is not a rectangular prism?

A.

C.

B.

D.

Difficulty: Medium

4. Which shape is a triangular prism?

A.

C.

B.

D.

Difficulty: Medium

5. Which shape is a triangular prism?

A.

C.

B.

D.

Difficulty: Medium

6. Which shape is not a triangular prism?

A.

C.

B.

D.

Difficulty: Medium

7. Which shape is not a prism?

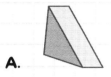
A.

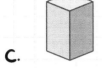
C.

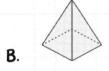
B.

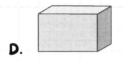
D.

Difficulty: Medium

8. Which shape is a triangular pyramid?

A.

C.

B.

D.

Difficulty: Medium

9. Which shape is a square pyramid?

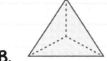
A.

C.

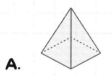
B.

D.

Difficulty: Medium

10. What is the base of the following shape?

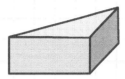

A. Pyramid
B. Square
C. Triangle
D. Circle

Difficulty: Medium

11. What is the base of the following shape?

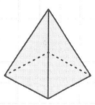

A. Circle
B. Rectangle
C. Triangle
D. Square

Difficulty: Medium

1. Explanation: A rectangular prism has six faces and has two bases that are rectangles. A rectangular prism can also have two bases that are squares that are connected by rectangles.

   The correct answer is B.

2. Explanation: A rectangular prism has six faces and has two bases that are rectangles. A rectangular prism can also have two bases that are squares that are connected by rectangles.

   The correct answer is D.

3. Explanation: A rectangular prism has six faces and has two bases that are rectangles. A rectangular prism can also have two bases that are squares that are connected by rectangles.

   The correct answer is C.

4. Explanation: A triangular prism has five faces and has two bases that are triangles.

   The correct answer is A.

5. Explanation: A triangular prism has five faces and has two bases that are triangles.

   The correct answer is B.

6. Explanation: A triangular prism has five faces and has two bases that are triangles.

   The correct answer is C.

7. Explanation: A prism has two parallel faces called bases. The prism is named by the shape of its base. Choice B is a pyramid, not a prism.

   The correct answer is B.

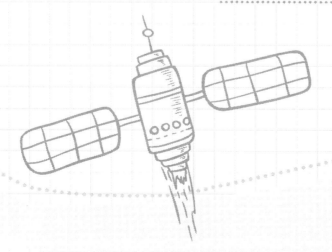

8. Explanation: A triangular pyramid has a base that is a triangle and faces that come to a point.

   The correct answer is B.

9. Explanation: A square pyramid has a base that is a square and faces that come to a point.

   The correct answer is A.

10. Explanation: The base of a shape is the surface or bottom that an object rests on. It can be the bottom but it can also be the top. The base of the prism is a triangle.

    The correct answer is C.

11. Explanation: The base of a shape is the surface or bottom that an object rests on. It can be the bottom but it can also be the top. The base of the pyramid is a square.

    The correct answer is D.

Mixed Assessment

1. Operations and Algebraic Thinking page

2. Numbers and Operations in Base Ten page

3. Numbers and Operations Fractions page

4. Measurement and Data page

5. Geometry page

BRAIN
HUNTER

1. What number is 4 less than 6?

A. 3   C. 4
B. 1   D. 2

Difficulty: Easy

2. 9 + 4 =

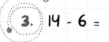

A. 11   C. 13
B. 12   D. 14

Difficulty: Easy

3. 14 - 6 =

A. 7   C. 9
B. 8   D. 10

Difficulty: Easy

4. 3 + 8 + 5 =

A. 15   C. 17
B. 16   D. 18

Difficulty: Easy

5. What problem can be used to help solve 1 + 3 + 9?

A. 1 + 9   C. 4 + 8
B. 2 + 9   D. 1 + 13

Difficulty: Easy

6. Last week, eight kids in our class were absent. This week, two kids in our class were absent. How many kids missed school over the past two weeks?

A. 9   C. 11
B. 10   D. 12

Difficulty: Easy

7. Which number is odd?

A. 27   C. 24
B. 22   D. 30

Difficulty: Medium

8. 17 + 7 =

A. 20   C. 24
B. 22   D. 26

Difficulty: Medium

 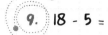

9. 18 - 5 =

A. 10   **C.** 12
B. 11   **D.** 13

Difficulty: Medium

10. Which choice describes the number of stars?

A. 6 + 2   **C.** 4 + 2
B. 1 + 5   **D.** 2 + 2 + 2

Difficulty: Medium

11. Which choice correctly describes the number of circles?

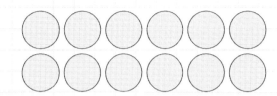

A. 4 + 2
B. 6 + 6
C. 12 + 6
D. 2 + 2 + 2 + 2 + 2

Difficulty: Medium

12. Mario has 14 seashells. He brings another 8 home from the beach. How many seashells does he have in his collection now?

A. 18   **C.** 22
B. 20   **D.** 24

Difficulty: Medium

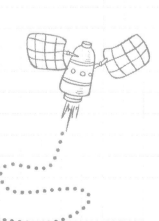

13. Elizabeth took **37** pictures over the past year. If she took **12** pictures in the last month, how many pictures did she take the rest of the year?

A. 25   **C.** 27
B. 26   **D.** 28

Difficulty: Medium

14. Which set of objects illustrates the problem **5 x 3**?

A.

B.

C.

D.

Difficulty: Hard

15. Which set of objects illustrates the problem **64 ÷ 8**?

A.

B.

C.

D.

Difficulty: Hard

16. 2 x 5 =

A. 10   C. 20
B. 15   D. 25

Difficulty: Hard

17. 36 ÷ 4 =

A. 10   C. 8
B. 9   D. 7

Difficulty: Hard

18. ? x 3 = 21

A. 6   C. 8
B. 7   D. 9

Difficulty: Hard

19. 48 ÷ ? = 6

A. 6   C. 8
B. 7   D. 9

Difficulty: Hard

20. Our family loves pizza. If there are six people in our family and we each eat 3 pieces of pizza, how many pieces do we eat in all?

A. 9   C. 15
B. 12   D. 18

Difficulty: Hard

1. Explanation: To solve this problem, you should count down 4 numbers starting at 6: 6, 5, 4, 3, 2.

   The correct answer is D.

2. Explanation: To solve this problem, you can count up 4 from 9, which will give you 13. You can also count all the vegetables together to get the result of 13.

   The correct answer is C.

3. Explanation: To solve this problem, you can count down 6 from 14, which gives you 8: 14, 13, 12, 11, 10, 9, 8.

   The correct answer is B.

4. Explanation: To solve this problem, you can break it into 2 separate addition problems. First, you should solve 3 + 8. To solve 3 + 8, you should count up 8 from 3: 3, 4, 5, 6, 7, 8, 9, 10, 11. Then you add 11 + 5. Count up 5 from 11: 11, 12, 13, 14, 15, 16.

   The correct answer is B.

5. Explanation: Order does not matter when you add. 1 + 9 + 3 is the same as 1 + 3 + 9.

   The correct answer is A.

6. Explanation: To solve this problem we need to add the numbers together. To solve 8 + 2, we count up two from 8: 8, 9, 10. The answer for this problem is 10.

   The correct answer is B.

7. Explanation: Even numbers are divisible by 2 and end in 2, 4, 6, 8, 0. Odd numbers are not divisible by 2 and end in 1, 3, 5, 7, 9. 27 is odd because it ends in a 7.

   The correct answer is A.

8. Explanation: To solve this problem, you should count up 7 from 17: 17, 18, 19, 20, 21, 22, 23, 24.

   The correct answer is C.

9. Explanation: To solve this problem, you should count down 5 from 18: 18, 17, 16, 15, 14, 13.

The correct answer is D.

10. Explanation: There are three lines of stars with two stars in each line. So to find the total number of stars, we should add 2 + 2 + 2, which equals 6. To check, count and you will see there are 6 stars.

The correct answer is D.

11. Explanation: There are two lines of circles with six circles in each line. So to find the total number of circles, we should add 6 + 6, which equals 12. To check, count and you will see there are 12 circles.

The correct answer is B.

12. Explanation: To solve this problem, you need to add the two amounts together. 14 + 8 is the same as counting up 8 from 14: 14, 15, 16, 17, 18, 19, 20, 21, 22. So the solution to the problem is 22.

The correct answer is C.

13. Explanation: To solve this problem, you take the total number of pictures she took, and subtract the pictures she took in the last month. The problem you are solving is 37 - 12. We can solve this by counting down 12 from 37: 37, 36, 35, 34, 33, 32, 31, 30, 29, 28, 27, 26, 25.

The correct answer is A.

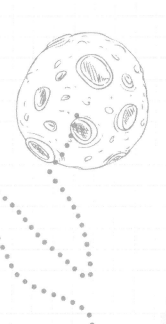

14. Explanation: When we multiply numbers, we are combining uniform sets of numbers. The problem **5 x 3** can be illustrated by drawing **5** groups of **3** objects.

The correct answer is B.

15. Explanation: When we divide, we are finding equal sets of groups. When we divide **64** by **8**, we are looking for how many equal sets of **8** we can find in **64**. The problem **64 ÷ 8** can be illustrated by dividing **64** into **8** groups of **8**.

The correct answer is D.

16. Explanation: To solve this problem, you should calculate **2** groups of **5**. One group of **5** is **5**, two groups of **5** is **10**.

The correct answer is A.

17. Explanation: To solve this problem, you should divide **36** into equal groups of **4**. When you break **36** into equal groups of **4**, you get a result of **9** groups.

The correct answer is B.

18. Explanation: To solve this problem, you need to figure out what number multiplied by **3** gives you **21**. Think about it in terms of groups. **1** group of **3** is **3**. **2** groups of **3** is **6**. **3** groups of **3** is **9**. **4** groups of **3** is **12**. **5** groups of **3** is **15**. **6** groups of **3** is **18**. **7** groups of **3** is **21**.

The correct answer is B.

19. Explanation: To solve this problem, you need to figure what number to divide **48** by to get **6**. How many equal groups of six can we make from **48**? When you break **48** into equal groups of **6**, you get **8** groups.

The correct answer is C.

20. Explanation: To solve this problem, we use multiplication. We should take **3 x 6**. **1** group of **6** is **6**, **2** groups of **6** is **12**, and **3** groups of **6** is **18**.

The correct answer is D.

1. What number is next in the following sequence? 52, 53, 54, _____

A. 55   C. 51

B. 56   D. 50

Difficulty: Easy

2. Which number is represented by the following tallies?

A. 12   C. 14

B. 13   D. 15

Difficulty: Easy

3. What number is 10 groups of 10?

A. 80   C. 100

B. 90   D. 110

Difficulty: Easy

4. Which number makes the comparison correct? _____ > 84

A. 81   C. 71

B. 91   D. 64

Difficulty: Easy

5. 82 + 9 =

A. 81   C. 90

B. 91   D. 95

Difficulty: Easy

6. 60 - 40 =

A. 100   C. 20

B. 10   D. 30

Difficulty: Easy

7. Which number completes the sequence? 617, 618, 619, _____

A. 619   C. 621

B. 620   D. 622

Difficulty: Medium

8. Which number is equal to 249?

A. 200 + 40 + 9
B. Four hundred, twenty-nine
C. 200 + 9
D. Two hundred, four, nine

Difficulty: Medium

9. Which number is equal to 5 hundreds?

A. 400 C. 50

B. 5 D. 500

Difficulty: Medium

10. Which number makes the comparison correct? 237 < _____

A. 93 C. 286

B. 185 D. 216

Difficulty: Medium

11. 270 + 100 =

A. 370 C. 470

B. 271 D. 280

Difficulty: Medium

12. 88 - 26 =

A. 62 C. 46

B. 64 D. 26

Difficulty: Medium

13. 35 + 14 + 79 =

A. 118 C. 127

B. 128 D. 137

Difficulty: Medium

14. Round to the nearest 10: 86

A. 60 C. 90

B. 80 D. 100

Difficulty: Hard

15. Round to the nearest 10: 43

A. 40   C. 70

B. 30   D. 90

Difficulty: Hard

16. Round to the nearest 100: 752

A. 760   C. 700

B. 750   D. 800

Difficulty: Hard

17. Round to the nearest 100: 919

A. 920   C. 940

B. 900   D. 1000

Difficulty: Hard

18. 40 x 7 =

A. 28   C. 110

B. 280   D. 320

Difficulty: Hard

19. 90 x 2 =

A. 11   C. 180

B. 110   D. 18

Difficulty: Hard

20. 5 x 60 =

A. 360   C. 30

B. 110   D. 300

Difficulty: Hard

1. Explanation: When you count, the sequence is as follows: 52, 53, 54, 55.

   The correct answer is A.

2. Explanation: 15 is correct because 15 is a bundle of ten and five ones.

   The correct answer is D.

3. Explanation: 10 groups of 10 gives you a ten in the tens place and a 0 in the hundreds place. It can also be represented as a 1 in the hundreds place, a 0 in the tens place, and a 0 in the ones place. Both of these groupings represent 100.

   The correct answer is C.

4. Explanation: First, you should compare the tens column. You are looking for a tens column that is equal or larger than 8. 81 has a ten that is equal to 84, but one is smaller than 4 so that doesn't work. The correct answer has to be 91 because that is the only number that has a ten and a one larger than 84.

   The correct answer is B.

5. Explanation: To solve this problem, you should count up 9 from 82: 82, 83, 84, 85, 86, 87, 88, 89, 90, 91.

   The correct answer is B.

6. Explanation: To solve this problem, count down by 10s from 60 four times: 60, 50, 40, 30, 20.

   The correct answer is C.

7. Explanation: When you count, the sequence is as follows: 617, 618, 619, 620.

   The correct answer is B.

8. Explanation: When you write 249 in expanded form, the correct response is 2 hundreds, 4 tens, and 9 ones. When you write 249 in words, the correct response is two hundred, forty-nine.

   The correct answer is A.

9. Explanation: One bundle of 100 is 100. Each additional hundred increases it by another 100. 5 bundles of hundreds is the same as 500.

   The correct answer is D.

10. Explanation: First you compare the hundreds column. You are looking for a number that is larger or equal to 2. 286 and 216 are both equal to 2 in the hundreds. You are looking for a number in the tens column that is larger than 3. 1 is smaller than 3 but 8 is larger than 3. So, 286 is larger than 237.

    The correct answer is C.

11. Explanation: This is the same as adding 27+10, which is 37. Then, you add the additional 10 for a final answer of 370.

    The correct answer is A.

12. Explanation: First, you subtract the ones. 8 - 6 = 2. Next, you subtract the tens. 8 - 2 = 6. This makes the final answer of 62.

    The correct answer is A.

13. Explanation: First you add 35 + 14. 4 + 5 = 9 and next you add 3 + 1 = 4. That makes a result of 49. Next you add 49 + 79. 9 + 9 = 18 You place the 8 and carry the 1. 1 + 4 + 7 = 12. The final answer is 128.

    The correct answer is B.

14. Explanation: To round to the nearest 10, you look at the ones column. 6 rounds the 8 up to 9.

    The correct answer is C.

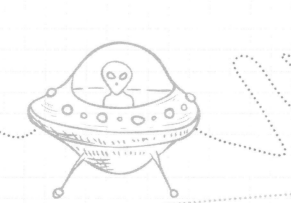

15. Explanation: To round to the nearest 10, you look at the ones column. 3 keeps the 4 at 4.

The correct answer is A.

16. Explanation: To round to the nearest 100, you look at the tens column. 5 rounds the 7 up to 8.

The correct answer is D.

17. Explanation: To round to the nearest 100, you look at the tens column. 1 keeps the 9 at 9.

The correct answer is B.

18. Explanation: To solve, you multiply 4 x 7, which is 28 and then add a 0 for the 40.

The correct answer is B.

19. Explanation: To solve, you take 9 x 2, which is 18 and then you add a 0 for the 90.

The correct answer is C.

20. Explanation: To solve, you take 5 x 6, which is 30 and then you add a 0 for the 60.

The correct answer is D.

1. Which circle is divided into **2** equal shares?

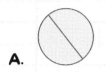

A.

B.

C.

D.

Difficulty: Easy

3. Which rectangle is divided into **2** equal shares?

A.

B.

C.

D.

Difficulty: Easy

2. Which circle is divided into **4** equal shares?

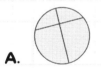

A.

B.

C.

D.

Difficulty: Easy

4. Which rectangle is divided into **4** equal shares?

A.

B.

C.

D.

Difficulty: Easy

5. Which fraction represents one part of the following drawing?

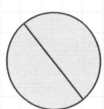

A. $\frac{1}{4}$ C. $\frac{1}{3}$

B. $\frac{1}{2}$ D. $\frac{2}{1}$

6. How many equal shares is the rectangle divided into?

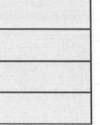

A. 2   C. 4

B. 3   D. 5

7. Which rectangle is divided into equal shares?

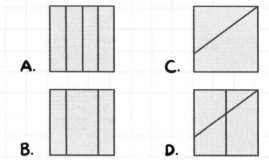

A.   C.

B.   D.

8. How many equal shares is the following rectangle divided into?

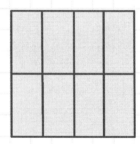

A. 6   C. 10

B. 8   D. 12

9. Which fraction represents one part of the following rectangle?

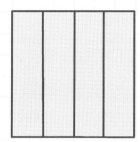

A. $\dfrac{4}{1}$ C. $\dfrac{1}{3}$

B. $\dfrac{1}{2}$ D. $\dfrac{1}{4}$

Difficulty: Medium

10. If a shape is divided into **5** equal parts, which fraction represents one part of the shape?

A. $\dfrac{1}{6}$ C. $\dfrac{1}{5}$

B. $\dfrac{1}{3}$ D. $\dfrac{5}{1}$

Difficulty: Medium

11. Which circle is divided into three equal shares?

A.   C.

B.   D.

Difficulty: Medium

12. Which word most accurately describes one part of the following rectangle?

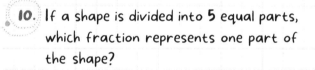

A. Half   C. Fourth
B. Third   D. Whole

Difficulty: Medium

13. Which fraction is equivalent to a half?

A. $\dfrac{1}{2}$ C. $\dfrac{1}{4}$

B. $\dfrac{1}{3}$ D. $\dfrac{1}{5}$

Difficulty: Medium

✷ Mixed Assessment ✷
✷ Numbers and Operations Fractions ✷

14. What is the value of the numerator of this fraction? $\frac{5}{8}$

A. 5   C. 3
B. 8   D. 13

Difficulty: Hard

15. What is the value of the denominator of this fraction? $\frac{11}{18}$

A. 1   C. 11
B. 8   D. 18

Difficulty: Hard

16. If the unit fraction is $\frac{1}{12}$, how many parts would the shape be equally divided into?

A. 1   C. 6
B. 12   D. 15

Difficulty: Hard

17. Which number should replace the ? to make the fractions equal?

$$\frac{1}{4} = \frac{?}{8}$$

A. 8   C. 2
B. 1   D. 4

Difficulty: Hard

18. Which number should be placed in the numerator of the following fraction to make it equal to 1?

$$\frac{?}{7}$$

A. 5   C. 7
B. 6   D. 8

Difficulty: Hard

19. Which fraction is the largest?

A. $\frac{4}{11}$ C. $\frac{4}{8}$
B. $\frac{4}{5}$ D. $\frac{4}{15}$

Difficulty: Hard

20. Which fraction is the smallest?

A. $\frac{6}{20}$ C. $\frac{11}{20}$
B. $\frac{8}{20}$ D. $\frac{20}{20}$

Difficulty: Hard

310

1. Explanation: This shape is the only one that contains a line that divides it into two smaller shapes of the same size.

   The correct answer is A.

2. Explanation: This shape is the only one that contains lines that divide it into four smaller shapes of the same size.

   The correct answer is D.

3. Explanation: This shape is the only one that contains a line that divides it into two smaller shapes of the same size.

   The correct answer is A.

4. Explanation: This shape is the only one that contains lines that divide it into four smaller shapes of the same size.

   The correct answer is B.

5. Explanation: This shape is divided into 2 equal parts. One part is represented by the 1 on top of the fraction and the two parts are represented by the two on the bottom of the fraction.

   The correct answer is B.

6. Explanation: The lines divide the shape into four smaller but same size shapes.

   The correct answer is C.

7. Explanation: This shape is the only one that contains lines that divide it into four smaller shapes of the same size.

   The correct answer is A.

8. Explanation: This shape contains lines that divide it into eight smaller but equal shapes.

   The correct answer is B.

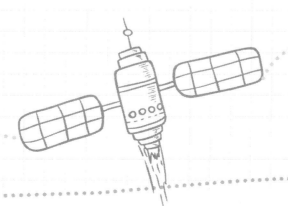

9. Explanation: This shape is divided into 4 equal parts. One part is represented by the I on top of the fraction and the four parts are represented by the 4 on the bottom of the fraction.

   The correct answer is D.

10. Explanation: If a shape is divided into 5 equal parts, each individual part would represent $\frac{1}{5}$ of the whole shape.

    The correct answer is C.

11. Explanation: This shape is the only one that contains lines that divide it into three smaller shapes of the same size.

    The correct answer is C.

12. Explanation: The rectangle is divided into three equal parts. Each part can be described as $\frac{1}{3}$ or one-third of the total rectangle.

    The correct answer is B.

13. Explanation: The fraction $\frac{1}{2}$ is expressed by the words "one half."

    The correct answer is A.

14. Explanation: The numerator of the fraction is the value on the top part of the fraction. It represents how many parts of the whole the fraction is representing.

    The correct answer is A.

15. Explanation: The denominator of the fraction is the bottom part of the fraction. It represents the total number of parts the item is divided into.

    The correct answer is D.

16. Explanation: The unit fraction $\frac{1}{12}$ represents a shape that is equally divided into 12 parts. We know this from the denominator of 12. The denominator of the fraction is the bottom part of the fraction. It represents the total number of parts the item is divided into.

The correct answer is B.

17. Explanation: Think about a circle that is divided into 4 parts. If you shade one part of the circle, you would cover the same area as if you divided the same circle into 8 parts and shaded 2 parts.

The correct answer is C.

18. Explanation: A fraction with the same numerator and denominator represents 1. In this case, since the denominator is given as 7, the numerator has to be 7 for the fraction to be equal to 1.

The correct answer is C.

19. Explanation: When comparing fractions with the same numerator, the larger the denominator, the smaller the fraction.

The correct answer is B.

20. Explanation: When comparing fractions with the same denominator, the larger the numerator, the larger the fraction.

The correct answer is A.

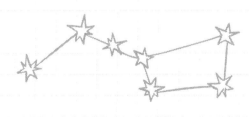

✳ Mixed Assessment ✳
✳ Measurement and Data ✳

1. Which object is the longest?

A.    C.

B.    D.

Difficulty: Easy

2. Which object is shorter than the arrow?

 A B C D

Difficulty: Easy

3. Which clock shows 2:00?

A.   C.

B.   D.

Difficulty: Easy

4. What is the time on this clock?

A. 6:08   C. 8:30
B. 6:40   D. 8:00

Difficulty: Easy

Use the below graph to answer questions 5 and 6.

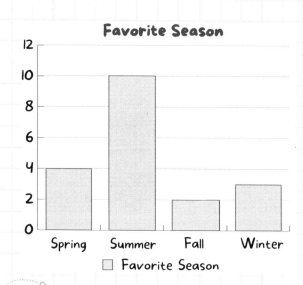

5. How many people were surveyed?

A. 29   C. 22
B. 19   D. 14

Difficulty: Easy

6. What is the most popular season?

A. Winter   C. Spring
B. Fall   D. Summer

Difficulty: Easy

7. Measure the line.

A. 5 in   C. 4 cm
B. 3 cm   D. 5 cm

Difficulty: Medium

8. Measure the line to the nearest $\frac{1}{4}$ inch.

A. 3 cm   C. $3\frac{1}{4}$ in
B. $3\frac{1}{4}$ cm   D. $3\frac{1}{2}$ in

Difficulty: Medium

9. What number should go in the missing box?

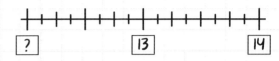

?   13   14

A. 11   C. 15
B. 12   D. 10

Difficulty: Medium

10. What time is on the clock?

A. 7:25   C. 7:05
B. 5:35   D. 4:45

Difficulty: Medium

11. If the scale of a graph says one ball= 6 students, how many students would be represented by $2\frac{1}{2}$ balls?

- **A.** 15
- **C.** 18
- **B.** 12
- **D.** 6

Difficulty: Medium

12. Mickey has only nickels to pay an arcade machine. If the machine costs $0.35 to pay, how many nickels will Mickey need?

- **A.** 6
- **C.** 35
- **B.** 7
- **D.** 2

Difficulty: Medium

13. Eleanor was 22 inches when she was born. She is now 46 inches. How much has she grown since she was born?

- **A.** 48
- **C.** 22
- **B.** 68
- **D.** 24

Difficulty: Medium

14. Which item holds around 1 liter?

- **A.** A coffee mug
- **B.** A medicine dropper
- **C.** A personal water bottle
- **D.** A pitcher

Difficulty: Hard

15. How many unit squares make up the area of this rectangle?

- **A.** 34
- **C.** 38
- **B.** 36
- **D.** 40

Difficulty: Hard

16. If the rectangle has a length of 12 and a width of 7, what is the area of the rectangle?

- **A.** 19
- **C.** 38
- **B.** 84
- **D.** 77

Difficulty: Hard

17. What is the time on this clock?

A. 4:09   C. 4:47

B. 5:45   D. 9:24

Difficulty: Hard

18. If each side of the following shape is 11 inches, what is its perimeter?

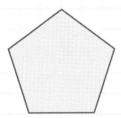

A. 55   C. 121

B. 44   D. 11

Difficulty: Hard

19. Our school day begins at **8:05 AM** and ends at **2:46 PM.** How long are we in school everyday?

A. 10 hours 51 minutes
B. 6 hours 51 minutes
C. 7 hours 41 minutes
D. 6 hours 41 minutes

Difficulty: Hard

20. We need **66** meters of fence to enclose our rectangular garden. If it has a length of **21** meters, what is the width of the garden?

A. 33   C. 12

B. 42   D. 24

Difficulty: Hard

1. Explanation: Choice D is the longest shoe as it takes up the most space from left to right.

   The correct answer is D.

2. Explanation: Choice A is shorter than the arrow. If you put them up against each other, choice A occupies not as much space as the arrow from top to bottom.

   The correct answer is A.

3. Explanation: To tell time, the small hand points to the hour and the large hand points to the minute. To show 2:00, the small hand should point to the 2 and the large hand should point to the 12.

   The correct answer is B.

4. Explanation: To tell time, the small hand points to the hour and the large hand points to the minute. To show 8:30, the small hand should point to the 8 and the large hand should point to the 6.

   The correct answer is C.

5. Explanation: To find the number of people surveyed, you need to add all the responses together. 4 people like spring best, 10 like summer best, 2 like fall best, and 3 like winter best. 4 + 10 + 2 + 3 = 19.

   The correct answer is B.

6. Explanation: The most popular season is the season with the most votes. 4 people like spring best, 10 like summer best, 2 like fall best, and 3 like winter best. 10 is the largest number so the most people like summer.

   The correct answer is D.

7. Explanation: To measure the line, you place one end of the line on the ruler and see where the end of the line falls on the ruler. If you do this correctly, the end of the line should fall on the 5 cm mark.

   The correct answer is D.

8. Explanation: To measure the line, you place one end of the line on the ruler and see where the end of the line falls on the ruler. If you do this correctly, the end of the line should fall on the $3\frac{1}{4}$ in mark.

The correct answer is C.

9. Explanation: On this number line, the number missing is before 13. The whole number before 13 is 12.

The correct answer is B.

10. Explanation: To tell time, the small hand points to the hour and the large hand points to the minute. To show 7:25, the small hand should point to the 7 and the large hand should point to the 5.

The correct answer is A.

11. Explanation: If 1 ball is 6 students, then 2 balls is 12 students. $\frac{1}{2}$ ball is 3 students. 12 + 3 = 15

The correct answer is A.

12. Explanation: Each nickel is worth 5 cents. To figure out how many nickels it will take to get to 35 cents, you should count by 5s until you get to 35: 5, 10, 15, 20, 25, 30, 35. It takes 7 nickels to get to 35.

The correct answer is B.

13. Explanation: To find this answer, you must subtract her original height from her current height: 46 - 22. 6 - 2 = 4 and 4 - 2 = 2, so she grew 24 inches.

The correct answer is D.

14. Explanation: A coffee mug, medicine dropper, and personal water bottle are all too small to hold 1 liter of liquid.

The correct answer is D.

15. Explanation: To find the area using unit squares, you count how many squares make up the larger shape.

The correct answer is B.

16. Explanation: To calculate the area, you can take the length times the width.

The correct answer is B.

17. Explanation: To tell time, the small hand points to the hour and the large hand points to the minute. To show 4:47, the small hand should point to the 4 and the large hand should point two marks after the 9.

The correct answer is C.

18. Explanation: To find the perimeter of a pentagon with a side of 11 inches, you add 11 + 11 + 11 + 11 + 11.

The correct answer is A.

19. Explanation: The easiest way to solve this problem is to count up from 8:05 to 2:05. When you do this, you get 6 hours. Then, you need to figure 46 minutes - 5 minutes, which is 41 minutes.

The correct answer is D.

20. Explanation: Perimeter is calculated by length + length + width + width. If our garden has a length of 21, we know that the perimeter = width + width + 42. The perimeter is 66, so we can determine that the two widths = 24. That makes 1 width equal to 12.

The correct answer is C.

1. Which shape has to have 4 equal sides?

A. Square   **C.** Triangle
B. Rectangle   **D.** Trapezoid

Difficulty: Easy

2. What is this shape?

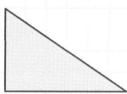

A. Square   **C.** Rectangle
B. Triangle   **D.** Trapezoid

Difficulty: Easy

3. Which shape is a trapezoid?

A.

C.

B.

D.

Difficulty: Easy

4. What is this shape?

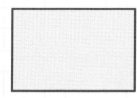

A. Square   **C.** Rectangle
B. Circle   **D.** Triangle

Difficulty: Easy

5. Which shape is a cube?

A.

C.

B.

D.

Difficulty: Easy

6. What is this shape?

A. Cone   **C.** Cube
B. Cylinder   **D.** Triangle

Difficulty: Easy

7. How many angles does this shape have?

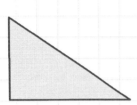

A. 1   **C.** 3
B. 2   **D.** 4

Difficulty: Medium

8. How many angles does a rectangle have?

A. 1   **C.** 3
B. 2   **D.** 4

Difficulty: Medium

9. Which shape has 4 right angles?

A. Triangle   **C.** Trapezoid
B. Square   **D.** Circle

Difficulty: Medium

10. Which shape has 1 circle face?

A. Cylinder   **C.** Sphere
B. Cone   **D.** Circle

Difficulty: Medium

11. Which shape is a pentagon?

A.   **C.**

B.   **D.**

Difficulty: Medium

12. Which shape has six sides?

A. Cube   **C.** Pentagon
B. Square   **D.** Hexagon

Difficulty: Medium

13. Which shape is a pyramid?

A.   **C.**

B.   **D.**

Difficulty: Medium

14. Which shape is not a quadrilateral?

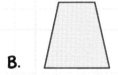

A.   C.

B.   D.

Difficulty: Hard

15. What is this shape?

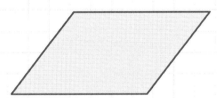

A. Square
B. Rectangle
C. Trapezoid
D. Parallelogram

Difficulty: Hard

16. Which shape is a rhombus?

A.   C.

B.   D.

Difficulty: Hard

17. Which shape is a polygon?

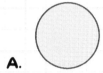

A.   C.

B.   D.

Difficulty: Hard

18. What is this shape?

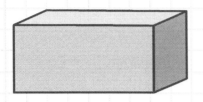

A. Rectangular Prism
B. Triangular Prism
C. Square Pyramid
D. Triangular Pyramid

Difficulty: Hard

20. What is the base of the following shape?

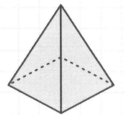

A. Circle   C. Square
B. Pyramid   D. Triangle

Difficulty: Hard

19. What is this shape?

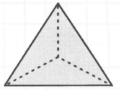

A. Rectangular Prism
B. Triangular Prism
C. Square Pyramid
D. Triangular Pyramid

Difficulty: Hard

1. Explanation: A rectangle is a shape with two sets of equal sides. A square is a shape with four equal sides. A trapezoid is a shape with two sides that go in the same direction and do not touch (parallel). A triangle is a shape that has three equal sides.

   The correct answer is A.

2. Explanation: A rectangle is a shape with two sets of equal sides. A square is a shape with four equal sides. A trapezoid is a shape with two sides that go in the same direction and do not touch (parallel). A triangle is a shape that has three equal sides. This shape has three sides, so it is a triangle.

   The correct answer is B.

3. Explanation: A rectangle is a shape with two sets of equal sides. A square is a shape with four equal sides. A trapezoid is a shape with two sides that go in the same direction and do not touch (parallel). A triangle is a shape that has three equal sides.

   The correct answer is D.

4. Explanation: A rectangle is a shape with two sets of equal sides. A square is a shape with four equal sides. A trapezoid is a shape with two sides that go in the same direction and do not touch (parallel). A triangle is a shape that has three equal sides.

   The correct answer is C.

5. Explanation: A cube is formed with six faces that are squares. A right rectangular prism has six faces that are rectangles, two of which may be squares. A cone is a shape that has a circle face and a curved bottom that comes to a point. A cylinder is a shape that has two circular bases and a rectangle curved middle that connects the two.

   The correct answer is A.

6. Explanation: A cube is formed with six faces that are squares. A right rectangular prism has six faces that are rectangles, two of which may be squares. A cone is a shape that has a circle face and a curved bottom that comes to a point. A cylinder is a shape that has two circular bases and a rectangle curved middle that connects the two.

   The correct answer is A.

7. Explanation: An angle is a corner where two lines intersect. Shapes have set amount of angles, which is one thing we use to define them as certain types of shape. Circles do not have any angles, triangles always have three angles, and squares and rectangles always have 4 angles.

   The correct answer is C.

8. Explanation: An angle is a corner where two lines intersect. Shapes have set amount of angles, which is one thing we use to define them as certain types of shape. Circles do not have any angles, triangles always have three angles, and squares and rectangles always have 4 angles.

   The correct answer is D.

9. Explanation: A right angle is where two lines intersect at a 90° angle. Squares have 4 right angles because each corner of a square measures 90°.

   The correct answer is B.

10. Explanation: 3-Dimensional shapes have faces. A face is the flat surface of any 3D shape. You can think of it as the surface that the shape could sit on. A cone has 1 circle face and a cylinder has 2 circle faces. A circle is not a 3 dimensional shape and a sphere does not have any faces.

    The correct answer is B.

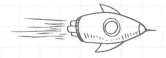

11. Explanation: A pentagon is a shape with five sides.

The correct answer is A.

12. Explanation: A hexagon is a shape with six sides.

The correct answer is D.

13. Explanation: A sphere is a shape that is round, which no flat bases. A pyramid is a shape with a base that is usually a square or triangle that comes to a point. A circle and a square are not 3-dimenisonal shapes.

The correct answer is C.

14. Explanation: Any shape with four sides is defined as a quadrilateral. There are many different types of quadrilaterals. A trapezoid is a quadrilateral with two parallel sides. A rhombus is a quadrilateral with 4 equal sides and opposite sides parallel. A rhombus with 4 90° angles is a square. A parallelogram has opposite sides parallel and equal. A parallelogram with 4 90° angles is a rectangle.

The correct answer is C.

15. Explanation: Any shape with four sides is defined as a quadrilateral. There are many different types of quadrilaterals. A trapezoid is a quadrilateral with two parallel sides. A rhombus is a quadrilateral with 4 equal sides and opposite sides parallel. A rhombus with 4 90° angles is a square. A parallelogram has opposite sides parallel and equal. A parallelogram with 4 90° angles is a rectangle.

The correct answer is D.

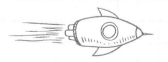

16. Explanation: Any shape with four sides is defined as a quadrilateral. There are many different types of quadrilaterals. A trapezoid is a quadrilateral with two parallel sides. A rhombus is a quadrilateral with 4 equal sides and opposite sides parallel. A rhombus with 4 90° angles is a square. A parallelogram has opposite sides parallel and equal. A parallelogram with 4 90° angles is a rectangle.

The correct answer is B.

17. Explanation: A polygon is a 2-dimensional figure with at least three straight sides and angles, usually having more than five sides. Shape B is a polygon because it has ten sides.

The correct answer is B.

18. Explanation: A rectangular prism has six faces and has two bases that are rectangles. A rectangular prism can also have two bases that are squares that are connected by rectangles.

The correct answer is A.

19. Explanation: A triangular pyramid has a base that is a triangle and faces that come to a point.

The correct answer is D.

20. Explanation: A square pyramid has a base that is a square and faces that come to a point.

The correct answer is C.

Made in the USA
San Bernardino, CA
01 June 2019